PRINTS AND DRAWINGS OF EDINBURGH

PRINTS & DRAWINGS
OF EDINBURGH

*A descriptive account of the collection in the
Edinburgh Room of the Central Public Library*

By

R. BUTCHART,

M.A., F.L.A.

formerly Principal Librarian, Edinburgh Public Libraries

C. J COUSLAND & SONS LTD.

Edinburgh

1955

Printed in Great Britain by
C. J. Cousland & Sons Ltd.,
30 Queen Street, Edinburgh

ACKNOWLEDGMENTS

In writing this descriptive account of the Print Collection in the Edinburgh Room of the Central Public Library I have received much assistance from various sources. The staff of the Edinburgh Room have been particularly helpful and Miss Marie A. Balfour, the Librarian in charge of the Department, has been most assiduous in checking dates and locating information about some of the lesser known engravers. I am also greatly indebted to her for reading the proofs and have to thank her most warmly for the care and attention she has given to these matters.

William Younger & Co., Ltd. have very kindly lent several of the blocks reproduced here, and Mr. J. B. Cairns has also been good enough to let me have the use of two blocks to illustrate early views of the City.

The printers and publishers, Messrs. C. J. Cousland & Sons Ltd. have given much consideration and thought to the presentation of the text and illustrations and have also lent a number of blocks.

To all these and to many others who have assisted me in my task from time to time I tender my grateful thanks. I have enjoyed writing the book and trust that it will prove of interest to the citizens of this great Scottish Capital.

CONTENTS

LIST OF ILLUSTRATIONS

ILLUSTRATIONS

EDINBURGH CASTLE FROM THE GRASSMARKET

Drawn by J. E. Ewbank and engraved by W. H. Lizars. 1825

THE EDINBURGH PRINT COLLECTION

TOWARDS the end of 1951 I wrote a short introduction to *The Edin-burgh Scene : Catalogue of the Prints and Drawings in the Edinburgh Room, Central Public Library*. It consisted of brief notes on some of the outstanding artists and engravers whose work is represented in the collection. It also dealt in some detail with the chief items illustrated in the catalogue, and mentioned in summarised fashion lists of prints of which there were particularly good examples. Several readers who have had occasion to use the catalogue kindly suggested that my short sketch might well be extended and that additional prints should be illustrated. The present volume attempts to meet the wishes of all those interested in the matter. It must be emphasised, however, that even this extended contribution only touches but slightly a subject which must appeal very strongly to all Edinburgh citizens as well as to those who are specially interested in prints and print collecting.

Since the seventeenth century Edinburgh has been a source of attrac-tion to artists, and their visits have almost invariably resulted in drawings, sketches, or prints which have considerable topographic or historic value, or illustrate in various ways the social life of the community. That need not cause surprise for few places in the country have a situation with viewpoints which make such a direct appeal to all gifted with the imagination of the true artist. An observant eye cannot fail to appreciate the scenic beauty for which Edinburgh is so justly famed.

The collection of prints and drawings in the Edinburgh Room at the Central Library has been gathered together during the last twenty-five years. It now numbers 3,600 prints and nearly 8,000 mounted illustrations, and undoubtedly ranks as the finest collection in existence of topographical and historical prints of the City. Though the collec-tion includes many valuable specimens of copper plate and steel engraving, aquatinting, lithography, etching, dry pointing, and other mediums it must be emphasised that the pictures have not been selected on account of their intrinsic value, but to show the development of the City from early times to the present day. An examination of the prints will reveal the changing face of Edinburgh much more clearly than any lengthy description can possibly hope to do.

In 1929 Mr. William Cowan, Chairman of the Libraries Committee and an expert bibliographer and collector, bequeathed to the Library his valuable collection of books and prints. The bequest formed the basis of the existing collection for, prior to that date, there were comparatively few prints in the Library stock; but with the opening of the Edinburgh Room as a separate department the numbers rapidly increased. Many other bequests were made and substantial gifts were received from time to time. Mr. Kenneth Sanderson, who succeeded Mr. Cowan as Chairman of the Committee, Mr. Charles B. Boog Watson, Mr. R. T. Skinner, Mr. John Russell, the Misses Ross, Miss Sylvia Steuart, and others were major contributors. In addition important purchases were made as opportunities arose—the Skene water colours; a number of unpublished drawings of Captain John Slezer, the author of *Theatrum Scotiae*; a sketch book of James Grant, the Edinburgh novelist and historian; a number of water colours by Mary Webster; and a set of coloured prints engraved by W. H. Lizars after drawings by J. Ewbank. Mention must also be made here of the collection of 88 fine prints bequeathed to the Corporation Museum in Huntly House by the late Sir Thomas B. Whitson, a former Lord Provost of the City. The Museum is now administered by the Libraries Committee and the exhibits include also notable prints and drawings by Mrs. Stewart Smith, Bruce J. Home, and other well-known artists.

PRINTS OF THE 16th CENTURY

IN beginning this account of the prints and drawings depicting the ancient Capital of Scotland, reference may first of all be made to an article, *Primitive Edinburgh,* contributed by the late Sir F. C. Mears to *The Early Views and Maps of Edinburgh, 1544-1852,* a publication sponsored by the Royal Scottish Geographical Society in 1919. In his article the author sought to reconstruct the lay-out and growth of the City from earliest times by means of diagrams and illustrations. Two of the latter are important—*Edinburgh in the eleventh century,* and *Edinburgh about 1460.* The former is a bird's-eye view from Arthur's Seat, looking towards the north west, showing the Castle and its suburbs on the ridge, the early roads and the beginnings of Holyrood and Leith. The latter is another bird's-eye view, looking due west from a point above St. Margaret's Loch. It indicates quite clearly the ultimate shape of things to come—The King's Wall, the Cowgate, and other historical points such as the enclosures of the Friars and Kirk of Field. These two illustrations are worthy of careful study and might well be the starting point for any consideration of the pictorial aspect of the Edinburgh scene down the ages.

Graphic description of the City begins about the middle of the Hertford 16th century. The earliest known print is the Bannatyne Club reproduction of a sketch in the Cottonian MSS. in the British Museum, illustrating the attack by the Earl of Hertford on the City in 1544. According to a footnote in volume 1 of the Club *Miscellany* " the lithographic facsimile is executed with great accuracy, and coloured in imitation of the original drawing, by Messrs. Engelmann, Graff, and Coindet, London. The colouring perhaps may indicate that the roofs of the houses in the City were covered with tiles, while those in the suburbs were only thatched." The surmise, on the face of it, is not very plausible, but lacking a better explanation it may perhaps be considered. The sketch bears a reasonable resemblance to later views of the town ; certainly it shows the great ridge along which the ancient burgh took its form. The viewpoint is from the north and the English forces are seen advancing to the assault from the slopes in the direction of the Calton Hill and entering the City via the Watergate at the lower end of the Canongate. A photostat negative of the sketch has also been secured for the Library collection.

In 1548 there was issued *The Expedicion into Scotland of . . . Edward, Duke of Somerset . . .* by W. Patten. It is concerned with Hertford's later invasion of Scotland in 1547 which culminated in the defeat of the Scots at the Battle of Pinkie. Patten's work was reprinted in *Fragments of Scottish History* by Sir John James Dalyell of the Binns, issued by Constable in 1798. The book contains three diagrams of very small size showing the disposition of the forces. The countryside between Musselburgh, Dalkeith, and Edinburgh is roughly indicated, and in the distance the crown of St. Giles is also shown. The sketches are so small that they have little or no practical value.

Münster Three years later, in 1550, a fantastic representation of the City appeared in Sebastian Münster's *Cosmographie*. The artist depicts towers and steeples stretching down on all sides from the Arx Puellarum [the Maiden's Castle] and the Ecclesia S. Cuthbert in the west to the Palatium Regis [Holyrood Palace] in the east, with the waters of the Forth and Letha [Leith] in the foreground. The print is one of those early engravings on which one must be careful not to place too much reliability. Skene of Rubislaw says " it is so little accurate in some of the principal *natural* features of the site as to lead to the supposition of its not having been constructed from actual survey, but suppositiously from the description which is more deserving of regard as being pretty accurate in its local details."

Darnley During the troublous times of 1567 there occurred that most
Murder disturbing incident in Scottish history which has led to so much controversy among historians—the murder of Darnley. A reproduction of a contemporary sketch of the scene of the murder at the Kirk of Field calls for mention here though it is still a matter of conjecture as to how far it represents correctly the surroundings in which this dastardly crime took place. One of the best of several reproductions is a coloured facsimile which appeared in a volume dealing with the Collegiate Churches of Midlothian issued by the Bannatyne Club in 1861. More recent attempts at reconstructiong the scene of the murder are those of

James Skene in his water colour *Kirk of Field* and an engraving by
J. Harris. For further details of the contemporary sketch readers are
referred to Cowan's *Early Views and Plans of Edinburgh* or Mahon's
The Tragedy of Kirk of Field.

Another early view of the City appears in an engraved copy of the Holinshed
sketch from Holinshed's Chronicle, published in 1577. It shows the
defence of the Castle by Kirkcaldy of Grange in 1573 in the interests
of Queen Mary. Batteries of cannon fire at the besieged from Princes
Street, St. Cuthbert's, High Riggs, Lothian Road, and other points.
The English troops under the command of Sir William Drury are
seen advancing through the ports in the City walls which are here
very clearly shown. While the siege was proceeding ramparts or
traverses were erected in the streets to protect the populace. These are
shown in the view. It is rather extraordinary to learn that Parliament
sat in safety in the Tolbooth and people went to divine service while
the siege was in progress.

The Castle rock is marked "570 feet highe"—a gross exaggeration
—and the North Loch appears with the designation *The Lough.* It is
also interesting to note that the Flodden Wall is accurately shown. The
print was reproduced in volume 2 of the Bannatyne Club Miscellany.

The next item of importance is the view of Edinburgh which Braun and
appeared in Braun and Hogenberg's *Civitates Orbis Terrarum* about Hogenberg
1582. It is obviously based on the above sketch without the warlike
effects, but with the introduction of four figures in period costume which
give character to the print. In 1817 this view was re-engraved by
Robert Kirkwood from the original in the *Theâtre des Cities du Monde.*
A smaller version of German origin with the addition of a moral
discourse on the futility of anger is taken from a book of morals issued
in 1631.*

These views of 1573 from Holinshed, and that of 1582 from the
Civitates Orbis Terrarum, show the Church of St. Giles with a
pronounced southern transept, although in fact it was never cruciform
and actually had no regular transepts. Mr. Ralph Richardson in
his article on Parliament Square in volume 3 of *The Book of the Old
Edinburgh Club* deals very fully with this error in these early views.

* See Cowan's *Maps of Edinburgh.* 2nd ed.

PRINTS OF THE 17th CENTURY

Van Dalen THE earliest of the 17th century prints is one by Cornelius van Dalen which forms the background to a fine portrait of Charles I on horseback. The topographical details of the City are merely incidental to the portrait. The Castle appears to the left and the towers of Holyrood on the right, while the houses in the Canongate, High Street, and the Cowgate are also lined in. Immediately above the view the word " Edynburgh " is printed. Van Dalen was a Dutch engraver who lived from 1602-65. The print probably represents the King entering the City in 1641, and it was no doubt issued about that date.

T. Pont Eight years later Blaeu's *Atlas* included a copy of Timothy Pont's map of the Provincae Lauden seu Lothien et Linlitquo. The original map actually dates from about 1610. On it there is engraved a very small and quaint picture of the City with its buildings close packed within the old Flodden Wall. Outwith the protecting wall the designations of such places as Marchistoun, Scheen, Kamron [Cameron], Wareston, Lyth, Sauchtoun, Gorgymill, and Laurencetoun [Lauriston], are clearly given. These early forms of many of the place names of districts now incorporated within the City boundaries will prove of interest to students of that engrossing subject.

Gordon of Rothiemay Although the two views just noted have a certain interest there is no doubt that the most important representations of the City of this period were the " bird's-eye " views and " prospects " to which the natural conformation of the burgh so readily lends itself. Of these the most striking example is the *Bird's-Eye View of Edinburgh from the South,* by the Rev. James Gordon of Rothiemay, who was invited by the Town Council to make a survey of the City. This print has been frequently reproduced, but none of the later issues equals the brilliance of the original engraving, a copy of which was presented to the Library by the late Mr. Kenneth Sanderson, and now hangs in the Edinburgh Room. It depicts the City in 1647 with its heavily built-up main thoroughfare, the Royal Mile, from the Castle to Holyrood. From a topographical standpoint its value is greatly enhanced by the key to the chief points of interest shown in the print, such as Parliament House, St. Giles, the Tron Church, Trinity College Church, George Heriot's Hospital, and other important landmarks. The City wall with its various ports at the Netherbow, Potterrow, Society, and Portsburgh, is clearly shown, and such details as the flesh stocks in the middle of the main street indicate that Gordon spared no pains to get an accurate as well as an artistic effect.

In his cautious fashion Mr. Cowan pointed out that care must be taken in referring to these early views since the places depicted are not always drawn to scale, and in this particular case he mentions that the town south of the High Street is shown in very full detail "but the portion between the High Street and the North Loch appears as just one continuous mass of buildings, the frontages and the roofs of the houses being shown in a merely conventional manner."

The print was engraved in Amsterdam by Frederick de Wit and the sheer beauty of the impression is a tribute to the excellence of his work. It appeared again about 1690 in a folio published in Amsterdam entitled *Theatrum Praecipuarum Totius Europae Urbium*. It was once more re-engraved and published by Andrew Johnston in London about 1710. Further issues appeared at different dates. These included an engraved facsimile of the original by Robert Kirkwood in 1817 and a lithographic facsimile by W. and A. K. Johnston in 1865, the latter being accompanied by a historical note by Dr. David Laing, a most useful bibliographical record of the view. Still another copy on a reduced scale was given in Sir Daniel Wilson's *Memorials of Edinburgh in the Olden Time,* 1891 edition, and other copies appear in whole or part in many modern works.

Later Gordon drew his two well-known "prospects" of the City from the north and the south, both engraved on one plate, entitled *Urbis Edinae facies meridionalis* and *Urbis Edinae latus septentrionale* respectively. They measure 20.6 by 7.5 inches. Again the detail is such that an excellent idea of the general lay-out of 17th century Edinburgh can readily be gained. Though Gordon was said to have been intensely dissatisfied with the work of the engravers on these plates they are quite good examples of copper plate engraving on such a large scale.

Presumably Gordon's interest in his subject was stimulated by his work on the plates described above, for he next drew four of the outstanding buildings of the burgh—the Castle, Holyroodhouse, Parliament House, and Heriot's Hospital—which were engraved together on one plate. These, as one might expect, lend themselves well to detailed treatment, and though a trifle formal in appearance are of such marked interest, both from the architectural and artistic standpoint, that they warrant further description here :—

(a) The Castle is designated the *Castrum Edinense quod &c. olim Arx Puellarum*. The view is from the west showing the precipitous rocky bank on which the Castle is built. The Half Moon Battery is seen to the east side. There is as yet no Esplanade, the construction of which was a gradual process during the middle years of the 18th century, as prints by Parr, Elphinstone, Sandby, and others clearly indicate.

(b) The engraving of Holyroodhouse is of particular importance since it is the only satisfactory view of the Palace as it was before the fire which took place during Cromwell's occupation in 1650 and represents the building as it was in the time of Mary Queen of Scots, and before alterations were made by Mylne for Charles II late in the 17th century.

(c) The Parliament House quarter of the plate shows that fine old structure now greatly altered and hidden away behind later buildings. Sited to the S.W. corner of St. Giles the façade showed admirably the elaborately designed doorway with the Royal Arms of Scotland and the sculptured figures of Justice and Mercy as supporters, and surmounted by turrets of Byzantine type connected by ornate balustrading. At the moment of writing the turrets on the south side of the building can still be seen from George IV. Bridge, but when the new extension of the National Library of Scotland is completed it is more than probable that the last glimpses of the stately and historic building will have vanished from sight.

An interesting story is told in Kay's *Portraits* about the two figures of Justice and Mercy. The Hon. Harry Erskine, Dean of Faculty, invited Robertson of Kincraigie, an eccentric Jacobite, to enter the Parliament House and see the Law

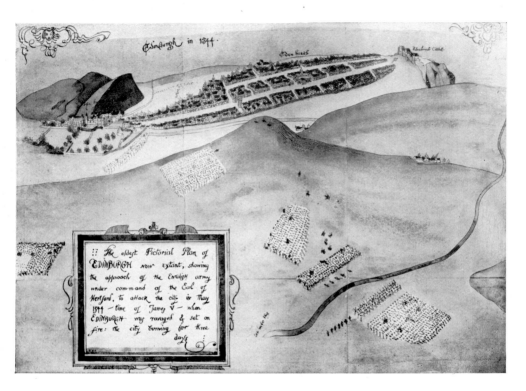

Edinburgh in 1544.

The oldest Pictorial Plan of
EDINBURGH now extant, showing
the approach of the English army
under command of the Earl of
Hertford, to attack the city in May
1544 – time of James V – when
EDINBURGH was ravaged & set on
fire: the city burning for three
days.

PLATE I

ATTACK ON EDINBURGH BY EARL OF HERTFORD
Reproduction of contemporary drawing, 1544

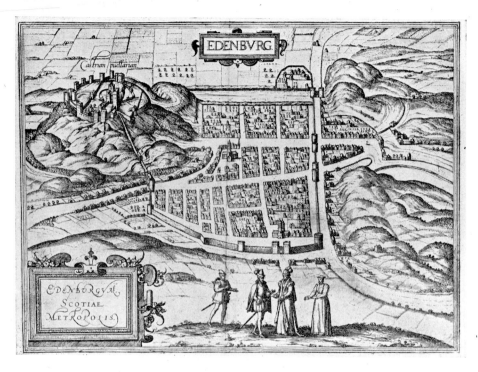

Castrum puellarum

EDENBVRG.

EDENBVRGVM
SCOTIAE
METROPOLIS.

PLATE 2

VIEW OF EDINBURGH FROM THE SOUTH
Engraving by Braun and Hogenberg. c. 1582

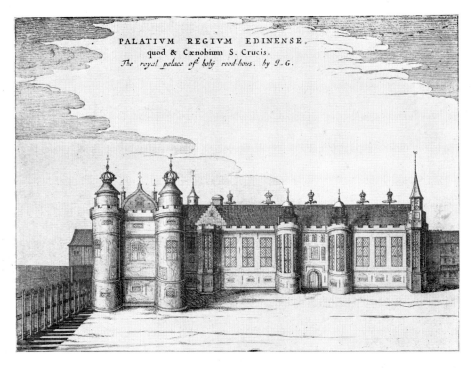

PLATE 3

THE ROYAL PALACE OF HOLY-ROOD-HOUS

Engraving by De Wit after J. Gordon of Rothiemay. c. 1649

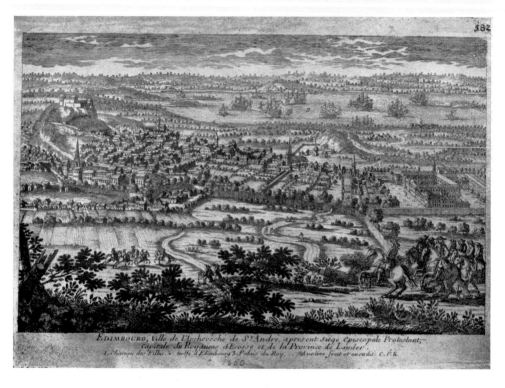

EDIMBOURG, Ville de l'Archevêché de S.t André, apresent siege Episcopale Protestant,
Capitale du Royaume d'Ecosse et de la Province de Lauder.
1. Chateau des Filles. 2. Golfe d'Edimbourg 3 Palais du Roy. Aveline fecit et excudit. C.P.R.
1650

PLATE 4

EDIMBOURG, VILLE DE L'ARCHÊVECHÉ DE ST. ANDRÉ
Etching by Pierre Aveline. c. 1650

Courts. The latter declined, saying, " But I'll tell ye what, Harry : tak in Justice wi' ye, for she has stood lang at the door and it wad be a treat for her to see the inside like ither strangers."

(d) Heriot's Hospital or *Heriott Orphanotrophium* as it is styled is very considerably different from the present day structure. The contract for the building was only placed in 1632, fifteen years before the date of the Gordon print. During that time the work was frequently held up and changes made in the original plans. The frontage with a lofty spire is seen from the Grassmarket side and the crenellated top of the City Wall appears at the back of the building on what is now Lauriston Place. There also appear two great towers surmounted by cupolas. James Grant speaks of these still being in existence as late as 1692 when the Town Council agreed to demolish them and replace them with a platform roof. That accounts for some of the differences which have puzzled many who have had occasion to refer to Gordon's picture.

Aveline

The next print to which reference must be made is an etching by Pierre Aveline with the lengthy title *Edimbourg, ville de l'archêveché de St. André, à présent siège épiscopale protestant, capital Royaume d'Ecosse et de la Province de Lauder.* The date is about 1650. Three places are numbered to indicate their relative importance—1. Chateau des filles; 2. Golfe d'Edenbourg; 3. Palace du Roy. Down from the slopes of St. Leonard's a number of horsemen canter, and further along one sees the winding road to Leith. Trees are everywhere both on the Edinburgh side of the Firth and in distant Fife. A conspicuous feature of the print is the great fleet of men-of-war anchored in the Firth. The etching is inscribed Aveline fecit et excudit CPR.

Den Hoyen

Following close upon the heels of Gordon and Aveline we have Rombout van den Hoyen, whose view of the City from the south is readily identified by the words *Edenburgum civitas Scotiae celeberrima* on the scroll at the top of the print and *Edynburgum* on the lower part. The date is apparently about 1650. At the bottom of the plate two horsemen are seen galloping along. The thinly built-up City between the Netherbow and Holyrood is well shown. Small figures are seen taking the road past the Calton Hill to Leith. A glimpse of Inchkeith and the hills of Fife complete the scene. At the bottom of the print is an eight line stanza printed in Latin, Dutch, and French.

Though Van Den Hoyen's work has not the same quality as that of Gordon or Hollar he serves as a link between these two fine engravers.

Two unsigned and undated prints, smaller in size but obviously based on Van Den Hoyen's engraving appeared much later as illustrations in the *Modern Universal British Traveller* and *Millar's New Complete Universal System of Geography* respectively, both engraved by Morris. The former bears the title *Perspective View of the Castle and City of Edinburgh, with the towns of Leith, Burntisland and Kinghorn,* and the latter *A General view of the City and Castle of Edinburgh, the Capital of Scotland.*

Hollar   It is interesting to compare Gordon's southern " prospect " with the photo-zincograph copy of an etching by W. Hollar dated 1670 entitled *The Citie of Edinburgh from the South.* Taken from the shoulder of Arthur's Seat this view depicts clearly the density of building within the City walls and the more spacious planning in the suburban area of the burgh of the Canongate. Beyond the City lies the broad green belt stretching to the Forth, with the hills of Fife beyond. Hollar, like Gordon, numbers the principal buildings and so materially assists in the identification of places of importance. According to a noted collector only four copies of the original print are known, none of which is in the City itself. The copy of this exceedingly scarce engraving in the Edinburgh Room is from part III of *Facsimiles of National Manuscripts of Scotland,* issued by the Ordnance Survey Office, Southampton, in 1871. It is dedicated in Latin by Johannes Ogilvius to the Magistrates of Edinburgh.

Merian   A photostat copy of a print by Matthew Merian with the caption *Edenburgum Edenburg* enclosed in an elaborate scroll is certainly of this period and resembles the Van den Hoyen or Hollar prints. It is an attractive general view from the south showing the whole area of the town and the countryside beyond, across the Forth, and away towards the Lomond Hills. The City Wall is clearly shown and the houses which had been gradually erected without it. A prominent feature at the foot of the print is a large group of figures with a farm wagon, a heavily laden packhorse, sheep, dogs, etc. An armorial shield surmounted by a crown is at the top of the print.

Yeates   An etching entitled *Prospect of Leith from the East* by Yeates is of more than usual interest since it is the earliest item in the collection relating to the Port. It can with certainty be dated 1682. It is a combination of plan and view with an inscription in these terms :—

> " Dedicated to the Right Honourable Sr. James Fleming, Lord Provost of ye City of Edinburgh and ye rest of ye Honble. Councill of the said Burgh. This map is humbly dedicated by Capt. Greenvile Collins, Hydrographer to the King."

The plan gives a clear view of the lay-out of the streets and the protecting breakwaters, while the view shows the Signal Tower and typical harbour scenes—all backed by a great range of buildings along the front.

In chronological sequence we next come to the views drawn by Slezer Captain John Slezer for his great work *Theatrum Scotiae,* issued first in 1693. It is well nigh impossible to over-estimate the value of these early topographical delineations of Scottish townships, and the two Edinburgh plates which occupy the place of honour at the beginning of the volume are excellent examples of early engraving. They feature the City from two aspects—from the south side of the Castle and from the Dean. The latter is notable not only for the fine view of the Village of Dean in the foreground, but also for the rather unusual picture of the North Loch. A later edition of Slezer gives a view of the City from the Calton Hill, much finer and in every way superior to those in the first issue of the work. A mint copy of this later view now hangs in the Edinburgh Room.

Slezer's work was greatly admired, but the heavy costs involved in engraving the plates proved too much for him and he was forced to apply to the Government for a grant to enable him to proceed with a continuation of the *Theatrum* which was to be called *Scotia Illustrata.* He was given a grant for five years of tonnage dues on ships exporting goods. This, however, was to be shared by John Adair, geographer, and in other ways was burdened by worrying restrictions. Slezer became more and more involved in financial difficulties and ultimately he was forced to take refuge from his creditors in Holyrood Sanctuary where he spent the last years of his life.

In spite of his financial troubles Slezer prepared many drawings which were unused for his *Theatrum Scotiae,* and others for the proposed continuation. In 1939 the Libraries Committee were fortunate enough to purchase for the print collection fifteen drawings which were almost certainly some of those so prepared, but not used. The titles of these pencil and wash drawings are as follows :—

Edenborrow and Lieth from the Island Enchkeith.
The Entry of the Castle of Edenburgh as it was in the year 1675.
The New Retrenchment within the Castle of Edenborrow.
The North Side of the Castle of Edinburg.
The Piere of Lieth.
The Prospect of the Castle and Citty of Edenborrow from the North Loch.
The Prospect of Edenborrow and Lieth from the Links of Lieth.
The Prospect of Edenborrow comeing from Musselborow.
The Prospect of Edinburow from Henry's Work [an error for George Heriot's Hospital].
The Prospect of Edenborrow from Listerreck [Restalrig].
The Prospect of Edenborrow from the Quarry Holes towards Leith.
The Prospect of Edenborrow from St. Anthony's Well.
The Prospect of Lieth from Lieth-wind at Edenborrow.
The South Side of the Castle of Edinburrow.
The West Side of the Castle and Citty of Edinburrow.

The drawings were apparently done about 1690. The quaint spellings of some of the sketches is characteristic of the period. The most unusual is Listerreck, an awkward rendering of the name of the district now known as Restalrig.

Slezer made some curious errors in titling his plates. The engraving of George Heriot's Hospital, for example, is called Bogen-Gight, being the seat of His Grace the Duke of Gordon near Aberdeen, and another drawing of Heriot's appears on the print entitled *The Prospect of Edinburow from Henry's Work*. For these and other errors it is difficult to account, but in spite of them one must recognize the fine quality and importance of Slezer's work.

Volume 2 of the Bannatyne Club Miscellany deals at considerable length with Slezer and his ambitious projects. One section sets out the " contents of the history and present state of Scotland, which is in readiness to be published by Captain John Slezer." Items 18 and 19 are detailed as follows :—

18. Funeral Solemnity of the Duke of Rothes, Lord High Chancellor of Scotland, represented in a most curious and exact draught, upon four sheets of Royal paper.

19. Cavalcade or Solemnity observed at the first Session of any Parliament in Scotland, as it was last performed by the late Duke of Queensberry, the King's High Commissioner, in the year 1685. Since which time there has been no such Solemnity; most neatly drawn on three sheets of Royal paper.

A footnote to this detailed list is in these terms :—

" The original drawings of these processions described in No. 18 and 19 were purchased for the Advocates Library, in 1803. One of them having been lost, its place was supplied in 1768, with a pencil drawing by Horace Walpole. From a MS. paper which accompanies them, it appears that they were obtained by the late Thomas Summers, glazier in Edinburgh, at a sale in London in the year 1766; and that afterwards he had them engraved and published by subscription."

Certainly there appeared in the Edinburgh *Evening Courant* of July 6, 1768, an advertisement of Summers relating to the proposals for etching these engravings. In the advertisement it is pointed out that the descriptions of the Cavalcades are based on information set out in Alexander Nisbet's *System of Heraldry,* a notable work which was published over a period of years from 1722 to 1742.

In the Edinburgh Room there are superb copies of these engravings of the processions on seven sheets of Royal paper, subscribed with the name of Alex. Kincaid. They are certified copies from the Lyon Record Office. Are these the engravings which Summers had done, and if so when were they issued ?

4

PRINTS OF THE 18th CENTURY

Few of the 18th century prints appear prior to 1750, but that is hardly surprising when one considers the state of the country after the Union of the Parliaments in 1707. Certainly conditions were not conducive to the development of the arts.

Cooper   Little is known of Richard Cooper, an Englishman who settled in Edinburgh during the early years of the century, and did most of his work there. He had a son of the same name, born in Edinburgh in 1730. They are represented by three prints in the Edinburgh Room:—

> Napier of Merchiston
> North Front of the Royal Infirmary
> West Front . . . of Holyrood House

As none of them is dated it is difficult to say whether they ought to be attributed to father or son, but as the younger appears to have concentrated on portraits it may perhaps be assumed that the above noted prints were done by the father who was an important figure in the history of Scottish engraving. He was born in 1705 and came to Edinburgh from London to visit a fellow artist, Alexander Guthrie. Apparently he liked the City and he soon showed his skill in engraving and draughtsmanship. He was active in connection with the Edinburgh School of St. Luke, an art school established in 1729, and acted as Treasurer for some time, but his chief claim to fame is that he trained Sir Robert Strange, one of the finest engravers of the time, and other skilled craftsmen. Cooper built a fine house in John Street, a private thoroughfare on the south side of the Canongate where many notable personalities were later to reside. He must have seen many of the prominent Jacobites from time to time, and in volume 2 of the *Book of the Old Edinburgh Club* there is reproduced in colour his engraving of Prince Charles Edward from the collection of W. B. Blaikie. Drawn in 1745 during his year of triumph the handsomely garbed Young Pretender is seen throwing down a Manifesto, while beneath the print is the note that " a likeness notwithstanding the disguise that any person who secures the son of the Pretender is entitled to a reward of 30,000 £ "

A rather scarce print, dated 1742, shows the surrender of Mary Queen of Scots to the Confederate Lords at Carberry Hill. The inscription on the scroll at the foot of the print is in these terms :— Carberry Hill

> The Battle-Array at Carberry Hill near Edinburgh with the surrender of Mary Queen of Scots to the Confederate Lords of Edinburgh, and the escape of Earl Bothwell, 1567. Done from the original now in Kensington Palace presented to the Royal Family by the Rt. Hon. Chas. Thomas, Earl of Pomfret, A.D. 1738.

For us the interest centres chiefly in the quaint picture of the City, with the tower of St. Giles seen from the north between the Castle rock and what is apparently meant to be Arthur's Seat. The heraldic banners carried by the troops indicate the part played by the nobility in the struggle. A small version of the engraving can be referred to opposite page 240 of *Mary of Scotland* by Grant R. Francis.

Early in the 18th century the Hon. John Elphinstone did fifteen sketches which were issued in book form under the title *Fifteen Views of the Most Remarkable Buildings of the City of Edinburgh.* Sold by Wm. Martin, Bookseller. Elphinstone lived from 1706-1753 and, though the volume is undated, the fact that one of the views represents the unfinished Poorhouse in Bristo enables us to determine the period as prior to 1740 since the building was opened in that year. Nine of the plates were engraved by Nathaniel Parr and one by Andrew Bell. Elphinstone

After Elphinstone's death the plates appear to have passed to Thos. Phinn who had his place of business in Parliament Square. Phinn later removed to the east wing of the New Exchange where he sold maps, prints, water colours, and artist's materials.

The views were used as illustrations for Arnot's *History of Edinburgh* published in 1779. In the second issue of that work plates 7, 8, and 12 were re-engraved and Phinn's name deleted from plates 3 and 9.

The Tron Kirk is the most interesting print since it gives a clear cut impression of the original façade and tower before the planning of the South Bridge ruined the architectural harmony of the structure.

In a recess of one of the east bays of the frontage there is a neat park for six sedan chairs. Other features include a family coach (six in hand, with postilions), ladies in crinolines, and water caddies, all of which combine to create an effective composition. That famous old building, the Black Turnpike, is seen on the right. At this period the Tron was the aristocratic church of the city and the élite attended the services regularly.

The series also includes a picture of the North Bridge which is worth comparison with later sketches of T. Donaldson, D. Lizars and others who were attracted by the artistic possibilities of the reconstruction work being carried out to bridge the eastern end of the North Loch; a view of Holyrood House from the south east showing the great range of windows on that frontage and the buttresses of the Abbey Church; and a *Prospect of the Gray Friers Kirk,* an animated scene in which many people, all stylishly dressed, stroll about the precincts of the church. The Library also possesses photostat copies of two wash drawings of the Castle, one of which is a large and detailed item measuring 34 inches by 21 with much useful information about the massive fortification.

The engraver was heir to the title of Lord Elphinstone but never succeeded as he died before his father. He published a map of Britain in 1744, and in 1745 a map of Scotland far in advance of anything that had gone before. During the '45 it proved most useful to both parties.

Bell   Shortly after Elphinstone's time we find Andrew Bell becoming associated with his friend Smellie, the founder of the *Encyclopaedia Britannica,* and ultimately becoming the sole proprietor of that great Edinburgh publication. Bell learned the art of engraving from Richard Cooper to whom he was apprenticed. His work consisted mainly of book illustrations. He is represented in the collection by his etching of Elphinstone's *Perspective View of the Parliament House and the Exchequer,* an undated print probably done about the middle of the century. Bell is said to have begun his artistic career by engraving names and crests on plates and dog collars, but he soon progressed far beyond that and did important engravings for Smellie's translation of Buffon in 1782. Latterly he amassed a fortune as a result of his speculation in the *Encyclopaedia Britannica.* He is said to have given an excellent training to his apprentices. In Kay's *Portraits* there is a

PLATE 5

NETHERBOW PORT

Water colour by J. Skene from a drawing by J. Runciman. N.d.

PLATE 6

VIEW OF EDINBURGH CASTLE FROM GREYFRIARS CHURCHYARD
Coloured engraving by P. Mazell after Moses Griffith. c. 1776

PLATE 7

PERSPECTIVE VIEW OF THE TRON CHURCH
Engraving by Hon. John Elphinstone. c. 1740

PLATE 8

SOUTH VIEW OF THE CANONGATE KIRK
Engraving by the Hon. John Elphinstone. c. 1740

character sketch of Bell who was sadly afflicted with his physical infirmities about which he was sometimes teased by his companions, but he was well able to keep his end up. Many good stories are told of him in Kay's work, showing him to be a man of pleasant disposition.

In this rough chronological sequence we now come to the brothers Runciman, painters and etchers in Edinburgh. Alexander, the elder, did a drawing, *East View of the Porch of Holyrood House,* about 1779 which was engraved by A. Cameron and used in Arnot's *History of Edinburgh.* Other than that he appears to have done little of a topographical nature, though he painted the ceiling of the famous Ossian's Hall at Penicuik House and did other work of a classical nature.

The younger of the two, John, died at the early age of twenty-four. He is remembered by his fine print of the demolition of the Netherbow Port on which James Skene and others based their own drawings of that subject. Like most artists the young Runciman had to turn his hand to all kinds of work and a photostat in the Edinburgh Room is copied from an elaborately engraved trade card for the Linen Hall, now Moray House. Within the ornate border is given a list of the types of cloth available for sale—lawn, cambrick, Fife linen, sheetings, and the like—with a note opposite each of the prices at which they could be supplied. At the top there is etched a small but well drawn picture of the Hall with the words ' Pro Patria, quod utilius ' as a motto set in the uppermost part of the card. The original print is in the British Museum (Gough Map Collections, No. 38). In the Bannatyne Club Miscellany there is also a reproduction of a view of Edinburgh done by John on the back of a playing card. A mere outline sketch, it was made from a chimney top station near the Tron Church.

Lumsden in his *Art of Etching,* claims John Runicman as " the first Scottish etcher of importance " and declares that by his early death " Scotland lost a great etcher prematurely." The Runcimans were sent to Italy in 1766 by Sir John Clerk of Penicuik, but long before that time John's artistic skill had reached such a stage that one must agree with Lumsden that he had etched many other plates round about the time when he produced his masterpiece of 1764. Where are these plates now ? Almost certainly some of them must have been devoted to Edinburgh subjects and it would be interesting to locate them.

Topham in his *Letters from Edinburgh . . . 1774 and 1775* makes mention of a Ridotto held in the Theatre Royal on 10th March, 1775, for which the decorations included, over the stage boxes, "landscapes done by Runciman, the Sir Joshua Reynolds of this country, and whose invention is perhaps equal to that of any painter in Europe."

Donaldson   Contemporary with the Runcimans was Thomas Donaldson who, about 1775, produced his *View of the New-Bridge of Edinburgh, with the adjacent buildings of the old and new town from the west.* This shows the drained Nor' Loch, the dykes, stepping stones across the marshy ground, a group of cattle to the west, and other features. The print was re-engraved by Daniel Lizars, a pupil of Andrew Bell, as an illustration for Arnot's *History,* but the book version is in every way poorer than the separate copper-plate.

Mercier   Towards the end of the century, in 1780 and 1781, Philip Mercier executed seven aquatints, very formal in appearance, of City subjects—the Castle, Heriot's Hospital, Holy Rood House, and general views from the east, south, north, and north west. In addition he is represented by a pen and wash drawing showing the front view of Heriot's Hospital. Of these aquatints the late Mr. Kenneth Sanderson said, "the set is met with sometimes in monochrome, and sometimes tinted by hand, and although crude in drawing there is a naïveté which is quite attractive. Mercier may have been resident in the city in some teaching capacity, but I have never come across anything else of his." In addition to the set of these aquatints in the Library another very fine set is exhibited in Huntly House. Cumberland Hill in his *Historic Memorials and Reminiscences of Stockbridge* reproduces two views which are apparently the work of Mercier. These are *View of Part of Old Stoke Bridge (looking west)* and *The Bridge at Water of Leith, about 1750 (looking west)* which are mentioned in the preface of that work.

This artist must not be confused with another with the same name who died about 1760.

Andrew Bell had as apprentices at one time or another the three
Robertson   brothers Robertson—Archibald, Alexander, and Andrew. All were painters and engravers and all spent some considerable time in New York.

Archibald lived from 1765-1835. He studied in Edinburgh and London where he was a pupil of Reynolds, but latterly he spent so many years in America that his Aberdeenshire and Edinburgh backgrounds tend to be forgotten. In 1795 he did a very fine aquatint of Edinburgh from the north west, after R. A. Riddell, a most attractive print from an attractive viewpoint. The Castle stands silhouetted against Arthur's Seat. In the foreground is a typical rural scene—a well wooded effect with a great tree on the left. To the extreme right Heriot's and the surrounding houses are lightly sketched in, and from the Castle itself there stretch down to the Firth in sequence Ramsay Gardens, the crown of St. Giles, the spire of the Tron, and other landmarks. While in New York Robertson published his *Elements of the Graphic Arts* in 1802 which was considered an important contribution to the subject.

Alexander was enthusiastic about landscape and etched some illustrations in the early *Scots Magazines* from drawings by Clerk of Eldin. It is probable that the following were his work :—

Craigcrook: drawn by F. Dick.	The Inch House.
Stockbridge and St. Bernard's.	Spylaw, near Edinburgh.

Only the Stockbridge cut is dated—1790—but they are almost certainly by the same engraver and about the same period. He also did views of Restalrig, Wryte's Houses, and Hawthornden. Alexander has another claim to fame since he was the master of Robert Scott, one of the great engravers of the time.

Andrew was almost wholly a miniature painter and consequently he is outwith the scope of this monograph.

The brothers used no initials on their prints or signed themselves simply as A. Robertson. That makes it a matter of some difficulty to identify the work of the trio since the initial A. could have been used by them all.

The next important engraver was Paul Sandby, an English artist Sandby who was commissioned by the Government, following upon the troubles of the '45, to make sketches to facilitate proposals for developing the country by means of roads, bridges, and other means of communication. Of the drawings done for this purpose the best known is his etching *East View of Edinburgh Castle* which dates from about 1750. The Castle stands out boldly against a clear sky. In most earlier views there is little evidence of the Esplanade as we now know it, but in this the building-up process has obviously been nearly completed. At one time a flight of steps led up to the drawbridge of the Castle, but when the ground was heightened and levelled up by the dumping of earth from the Royal Exchange site, and from other excavations in progress for the development of the New Town, the steps were found to be unnecessary. In the print there is a scene of great activity at the eastern end of the parade ground where a picturesque group in contemporary costume watch keen contestants 'putting the stane,' a characteristic Scottish athletic pastime which is still practised in the Highland Games of the present day.

While the east view described above is undoubtedly a fine and accurate piece of work the claim for topographical accuracy cannot be made for his companion picture *West View of the City of Edinburgh* done in 1753. The title is also given in French—*Vue Occidentale de la Ville d'Edinbourg*. Of this print Mr. William Cowan says :—

> " The position of Arthur's Seat and the Crags is quite wrong, and the delineation of the Old Town in a curve following the line of the Crags, has very little resemblance to the actual fact. It is also pretty certain that no such formal rows of trees as appear in the foreground ever existed."

In spite of this damaging pronouncement it cannot be denied that the print is an attractive and artistic composition, and on several occasions it was copied, sometimes with minor alterations. One of these copies was done for the *New Geographical Dictionary*. It is inscribed— Hulett, fect. Whereas in the original Sandby print three figures are grouped round a rock in the foreground, in this copy these are replaced by three fashionably dressed 18th century young men. A farmer's waggon has also been introduced and there are other minor changes. In another copy engraved for Barlow's *General History of Europe* the three figures are again changed and in this case the fashionably dressed young men are reduced in number to one Highlander and one other bystander, while the farmer's waggon has been discarded.

Another view, this time *A Perspective View of the Eastern Side of the Castle,* presents a rather different impression of the great fortress. It was engraved by P. Fourdrinier for Maitland's *History of Edinburgh*. The raising of the level of the Esplanade is in progress and is about half finished. The main gateway of the Castle appears with the mechanism for operating the portcullis over the dry moat. There are figures on the right at the head of the steep slopes down to the North Loch while in the distance, to the right, can be seen several houses, including the Earl of Moray's residence, Drumsheugh House.

Fourdrinier engraved a number of Sandby's other sketches of 1753 for Maitland's *History of Edinburgh,* including *Trinity College Church, View of Leith from the East Road,* and *Surgeon's Hall.* The Leith item provides a charming study of the Edinburgh stage coach on its way to Leith, with a view of the Port itself and the Firth beyond. Another point of interest arises in the *Perspective View of the Surgeon's Hall.* The print in Maitland shows the elevation of the building with eight small figures in the foreground. James Grant used the view in volume 1 of *Old and New Edinburgh* but no fewer than twelve of John Kay's characters are superimposed in his version of the engraving. Why this was done one can only surmise but it rather spoils the effect of the print.

Many of Sandby's drawings are listed in the catalogue of prints and drawings in the British Museum and eight of them have been copied by the rotograph process for the Library collection.

Sandby produced a volume entitled *The Virtuosi's Museum,* 1778, which includes a fine print of Edinburgh Castle engraved by F. Chesham. Oddly enough the impression of the print in the Library is dated 1779. The Castle is set in an oval frame. At the foot of the picture two figures are reclining on either side of a pediment on which is a vase of classical design. The volume contains views of Lanark, Glasgow, Stirling, and other well-known places. Each plate has a brief note attached and the Edinburgh illustration gives the following information :—

> " It was formerly called the Maiden Castle, because the Pictish Kings kept their daughters there. Still more anciently it was called Alatum Castrum, or the Winged Castle, perhaps from its form, and standing on so high a hill, as it were in the air. . . .
>
> A chapel is also in it for the use of the garrison; and it is furnished with water by two wells in the rock. From the Castle is a delightful prospect over the City and neighbouring country; and to the river of Forth, from whence it is saluted by such men of war as come to anchor in Leith Road. The Governor is always a person of prime quality, and general of the forces."

In 1947 the Phaidon Press issued A. P. Oppé's important work *The Drawings of Paul and Thomas Sandby in the Collection of His Majesty the King at Windsor Castle* which will prove of the utmost value for research workers in this field. Three drawings included relate to Edinburgh. They are

(a) A Humble Imitation of Vauxhall in the grounds of Heriot's Hospital, Edinburgh. It shows a typical garden party scene with strollers in fashionable dress and the ladies in their wide spreading crinolines. Heriot's is in the background to the left faintly sketched in.

(b) A sketch of Allan Ramsay " seated in hat and blue dressing gown at a table and smoking a Turkish pipe which is elongated in caricature to reach diagonally across the drawing."

(c) A Street Coffee House, Edinburgh. On the left a man dressed in pink with blue waistcoat advances with head bent, while beyond, a small square erection like a watchman's booth is seen with five men seated in discussion on low benches around it.

The above and other sketches relating to the City show that Sandby, during his stay in Scotland, did a very considerable amount of work of high quality. He is also known to have been one of the pioneers in the new process of aquatinting in which he developed remarkable skill and found that the new method was particularly adapted to the reproduction of water colour sketches.

In discussing Sandby's Edinburgh work Oppé speaks of the Heriot's Hospital drawing noted above in the following terms :—

" The little drawing of the grounds of Heriot's Hospital is only incidentally a landscape; the interest is mainly in the groups of figures which crowd the foreground and middle distance, and show an ease in their disposal and minuteness in execution which recall the gouache drawings of Blarenbergh. Paul Sandby produced more important landscapes, some of which he engraved and published on his return to London in 1751; and in at least one water colour of Edinburgh, dated 1751, which made a brief appearance in the market in the darkest days of 1941, even greater crowds of neatly drawn figures had for their background the Rock and Castle of Edinburgh drawn with as much delicacy as the Heriot's Hospital, and coloured with the gay pinks and blues with which the distances are sweetened in the landscapes of both brothers."

In Cowan's *Early Views* (No. 22) there is an account of a fanciful view of the City issued by the house of Basset in Paris. It is almost certainly somewhat later than Sandby. The inscription ' Edimbourg ' is followed by a note in French descriptive of the Capital and a series of fourteen numbered references to the places shown in the engraving. Thus 2 is Le Grand Temple, 5 Le Chateau, and 8 Le Petit Leyth, Port de Mer d'Edimbourg, and so on. The general effect of the view is so fantastic that it has no topographical value whatever, and Mr. Cowan was of the opinion that the engraver had overlooked the necessity to reverse the draughtsman's sketch. Even that explanation can hardly account for the extraordinary effect produced. Basset

At a later date this same French publishing house produced a series of exceedingly formal and equally inaccurate pictures of the City. One of them purports to be a *Vue de l'église St. George's à Edimbourg* though it actually represents St. Andrew's at the east end of George Street. The others are no better and it would probably be charitable to assume that the artist had been relying too much upon an extremely unreliable memory for his impressions of the City. The other places included in the set are the Grassmarket, St. Giles, the Castle, Princes Street, and the Calton Hill. The latter is entitled *Vue de la place et de la colonne Nelson à Edimbourg*. Alongside the column is the National Monument completed. The print is hand coloured and has some figures in period costume.

At this point the pencil and wash drawings of Richard Gough, the noted English antiquary are worthy of note. He lived from 1735-1809 and found great pleasure in touring both at home and abroad, in connection with his antiquarian researches. While on his travels he placed on record his impressions of the places he visited and as he was quite facile with his pencil the resulting sketches were of considerable topographic importance. He visited Scotland in 1771 and must have spent some time in Edinburgh. Much of his original work is lodged in the Bodleian Library, Oxford, but rotographs of 18 of his sketches are in the Edinburgh Room, among them a copy of the notable wash drawing entitled *St. Giles from the Parliament Square* which is reproduced here. The view is from the south and shows the old shops and dwellings clustering around the walls of the church. This square was noted for the many shops of jewellers, goldsmiths, engravers, and other craftsmen who dispensed their wares in the ' Heart of Midlothian.' Gough

Heart of
Midlothian

Alongside it might well be placed the fine lithograph of that title, the work of W. and A. K. Johnston in 1852 which illustrates perfectly the street life of the Capital in the middle of the 18th century. It is a lively and most attractive print, with a note at the bottom giving the following historical details :—

> " The Tolbooth from a very early period had been used for the meetings of the Scottish Parliament, and the Courts of Justice. It was repaired in 1561 and for a long period anterior to its removal in 1817, had been used solely as a prison for debtors and criminals, and as the quarters of the City Guard."

Original drawings, models, etc. formed the basis for the engraving.

Another most interesting aquatint centred on this area is *Parliament Close and Public Characters of Edinburgh fifty years since* after a painting by Sir David Wilkie and others, engraved by John Le Conte and etched by T. Dobbie. Alexander Fraser and William Kidd are said to have collaborated with Sir David in painting the figures which were based on Kay's *Portraits,* while David Roberts and John Wilson filled in the architectural details. Surely few other pictures have been completed by so many eminent artists. The figures from Kay's *Portraits* include such well known characters as John Dowie, Lang Sandy Wood, Hugo Arnot, and Dr. Gregory of mixture fame. The grouping of the figures is very striking. Part of Parliament House is seen on the left with the Goldsmith's Hall adjoining it. Behind, the towering mass of the Cathedral with its quaint ' lean-to ' shops occupied by the clockmakers, jewellers, and goldsmiths already referred to, dominates and dwarfs everything in the vicinity. The aquatint is in the Edinburgh Room and the original painting hangs in Huntly House.

Gilpin   William Gilpin was a writer who viewed Edinburgh in quite a different way from the usual traveller to Scotland and his trenchant criticisms as set down in his *Observations relative chiefly to Picturesque Beauty made in the year 1776* must have come as a great surprise to the citizens who were so accustomed to more favourable comments. In his book there are two aquatints, the first of which shows the approach to Edinburgh from the direction of Dalkeith. According to Gilpin " Arthur's Seat and the rocks about Edinburgh present, at a distance, the appearance of a cap of maintenance in heraldry, and a view with

PLATE 9

VIEW OF LEITH FROM THE EAST ROAD
Etching by Paul Sandby. 1751

PLATE 10

EAST VIEW OF EDINBURGH CASTLE
Etching by Paul Sandby. c. 1750

PLATE II

St. Giles from Parliament Square
Wash drawing by R. Gough. c. 1771

PLATE 12

THE HEART OF MIDLOTHIAN
Lithograph by W. and A. K. Johnston.   1852

such a staring feature in it can no more be picturesque than a face with a bulbous nose can be beautiful."

Of the second view—a corner of the rock on which Edinburgh Castle stands with the bridge over the North Loch—he is equally uncomplimentary. "Scarce anything in it deserves the least attention; except the views from the batteries, which are very amusing; particularly those over the Forth. The bridge over the North Loch is introduced in the distance like a Roman aquaduct."

Still another unusual statement is to the effect that "Arthur's Seat presents an unpleasing view from every station. . . . It's great regularity has in part been owing to the streets of London; which were paved from its bowels. A girdle of quarry running round it, adds to its formality."

Obviously Gilpin had no feeling for the use of words. Had he stayed longer in the City he might have seen something more of it and would then have been better qualified to speak more favourably of the Capital's attractions.

An important contributor to the Edinburgh scene was Thomas Hearne, one of those itinerant draughtsmen who were frequently commissioned by wealthy patrons to accompany them on their grand tours. He lived from 1744-1817 and began life as an engraver with William Woollett. Later he went with Lord Lavington to the Leeward Islands where he served as draughtsman to the Governor from 1771-1775. On his return to England he set to work on his most important project *The Antiquities of Great Britain*. Hearne was particularly attracted by Gothic architecture combined with landscape, and his great work is a landmark in the history of topographic drawing and engraving. Most of the plates were engraved by W. Byrne about 1780. These include the Castle, Holyrood, Craigmillar, and St. Anthony's Chapel. The dominating feature of the Castle print is the Half Moon Battery with the steep rocky road leading up to it and the towering mass of the other buildings behind. The Chapel on the slopes of Arthur's Seat is also a bold piece of drawing. Between the ruined walls of the structure a woman is setting out her washing on the greensward while straight ahead is an open view of the City ridge with terrace above terrace rising to the Castle on the summit. Hearne was evidently greatly fascinated by the picturesque Edinburgh sky-line and he uses it to good effect in these masterly impressions of the Capital.

25

Adam of
Cardonnel

Practically contemporary with Hearne we have Adam of Cardonnel, an amateur etcher of some importance. He was fortunate enough to have the opportunity of joining Grose in his Scottish journeys and no doubt he also was keen to 'tak' notes' of the beautiful scenes through which he and his scholarly friend were passing. The result was his *Picturesque Antiquities of Scotland* published in 1788 which comprised a series of plates of famous ecclesiastical and baronial edifices. Under all the etchings are notes outlining the historical and other features of the prints. They are alphabetically arranged and the Edinburgh items include views of the Castle, Holyrood, Restalrig Church, St. Anthony's Chapel, and Craigmillar, of which there are three plates. Despite their small size the details of each subject are etched in most careful fashion. Cardonnel did other kinds of engraving and he made a notable contribution to numismatics with his sheets of plates for *Numismata Scotiae,* issued in 1786. Cardonnel was the first Curator of the Society of Antiquaries of Scotland from 1782-1784. On succeeding to the Chirton estate he changed his name to Lawson and a certain amount of confusion has thereby arisen.

Nicholson

About this time F. Nicholson was working in Edinburgh and in 1798 he drew a view of Edinburgh which was engraved by J. Walker. Nicholson lived from 1753-1844 and he was a most prolific worker for he is stated to have done 800 drawings on the stone. As a teacher he exercised a profound influence on his pupils. In the view noted above we have a vivid picture of the buildings fronting the Castle and some rather quaint figures on Bruntsfield Links. Nicholson also did a boldly executed aquatint entitled *Edinburgh Castle from the Grassmarket.* The date is approximately 1810. It presents a characteristic study of life in the Grassmarket at a period preceding the formation of Johnston Terrace. To the left is the striking building with crow-stepped gables and quaint dormer windows known as Borland's House; beyond it the exit from the Market by King's Stables Road; and on the extreme right the Boughts Custom House which was later demolished to make way for the old Corn Market. In the background looms the great Castle rock and the massive fortress with the well known view of the Half Moon Battery.

Farington

Joseph Farington visited Scotland in 1788 and 1792. On June 24th, 1788, he tells us that he " made a circuit through part of the New Town, round the Castle, but the rain prevented my proceeding. Under the disadvantage of seeing objects in such weather, the Castle and Rock upon which it is situated far exceeded my expectation. Both in respect of form and colour it is picturesque beyond any object which I have before seen. In many points of view it is perfect as a composition, and the grace and colour of the Rock and that sobriety of tone which time has given to the buildings is admirably consistent with the magnificence of the forms." Two days later he records in his diary his opinion that " The South or South East angle of the Castle is greatly superior to any other view of it, though it is magnificent everywhere. After examining the situations near the Castle I went along the road to Queensferry which is west from the Castle, and after walking over a beautiful situation at abt. ½ a mile from the Castle where the Earl of Moray has a House, and a small tract of ground which he has laid out neatly, and passed a walk through, I was surprised to find myself on the banks of a dell at the bottom of which runs a Brook called Leith water. It is very romantic, particularly near some mills where a Bridge is thrown over a stream that is a little below."

These walks round the City resulted in his fine views of the Castle, Holyrood, and other places, nineteen photostats of which are in the Edinburgh Room, including one of his superb *East View of Edinburgh Castle*. But he is best represented by his beautiful *North West View of Edinburgh Castle from the Water of Leith* which was engraved in coloured aquatint by F. Jukes. This lovely print is notable for its soft tones. The placid surface of the river; the young man, watched by his parents, fishing from the bank; and the varying tints of the tree foliage make a most pleasing rural landscape. The Castle, with the tall buildings of the Royal Mile, fill the centre background, and there are distant glimpses of Heriot's Hospital and Arthur's Seat on the right.

Part of Farington's manuscript diary relating to his visit to Edinburgh is in the Edinburgh Room where it may be consulted for further details of this noted artist's tour to places in Scotland.

Two other views of the Castle were drawn and etched by Farington. These were his *South East View of Edinburgh Castle* and *East View of Edinburgh Castle*. The first is a typical Farington sketch with the Castle etched in outline. Below the precipitous rock is a cottage with tiled roof. Four figures are seen in the foreground and to the left some trees give a rural touch to the scene. The second must not be confused with the *East View* already mentioned. This is really more from the south east. The Castle is again in outline and several country cottages are introduced with a dry stane dyke in front. This nicely coloured copy gives an excellent impression of the locality before Johnston Terrace and the King's Bridge were constructed.

Sparrow   In 1788 and 1789 Sparrow was engaged by Captain Francis Grose to do a number of cuts for his noted work, *The Antiquities of Scotland, 1797*. The engraver's contribution of Edinburgh views numbered nine, including a very fine picture of the Castle from the south east. The others were :—

> Abbey and Palace of Holyrood House
> Holyrood Chapel, west aspect
> Inside of Holyrood Chapel
> St. Roque's Chapel
> The Wryte's Houses
> St. Anthony's Chapel
> Craig Miller Castle (2 prints)

James Newton collaborated with Sparrow and produced the following plates :—

> The Well-House Tower, Edinburgh Castle
> Herriot's Hospital
> Trinity Colledge Church, Edinburgh
> St. Anthony's Chapel
> Restalrig Church
> Craig Miller Castle
> Cross at Edinburgh (showing Luckenbooths)
> Marchiston Tower
> Edinburgh Castle

As Grose was accompanied by Adam de Cardonnel for at least some part of his tour he was well advised on the artistic aspects of the places visited. The engravings were each approximately 7 by 5 inches and were published by S. Hooper.

Allan   David Allan, a noted painter and engraver, was born in 1744 at Alloa and in 1786 became head of the Edinburgh Academy of Arts, a position which he occupied until his death in 1796. A Scottish pioneer of aquatint engraving, he is said to have been taught the art by Paul

Sandby. His most important works were done towards the end of his life. They include a fine portrait of Allan Ramsay and ten illustrations, all in aquatint, for the 1788 edition of *The Gentle Shepherd,* issued by Foulis of Glasgow. This was the edition referred to by Burns in his letter dated 3rd March, 1794 to Alexander Cunningham from Dumfries. Burns writes " by-the-bye, do you know Allan ? He must be a man of very great genius. Why is he not known ? Has he no patrons ? Or do ' poverty's cold wind and crushing rain beat keen and heavy on him ' ? I once, and but once, got a glance of that noble edition of the noblest pastoral in the world; and dear as it was, I mean dear as to my pocket, I would have bought it: but was told that it was printed and engraved for subscribers only. He is the only artist who has hit genuine pastoral costume."

The copy of this edition of Ramsay's pastoral in the Edinburgh Public Libraries was presented to Burns by Alexander Cunningham on 4th April, 1794. It is inscribed " to Mr. Robert Burns, to whom his Country is indebted for the best Pastoral and Lyric Poetry of the Age, this copy of *The Gentle Shepherd* is presented by his enthusiastic and sincere friend A. Cunningham."

Four of Allan's prints are worthy of special note. They are :—

(a) *The General Assembly of the Kirk of Scotland.* Issued in 1783 this etching illustrates his interest in church affairs. It is provided with a key which enables one to identify the notable personalities who dominated the ecclesiastical affairs of Scotland at that time. The Earl of Dalhousie occupies the chair of honour and others in the picture include the Moderator, Dr. Spence; Principal Robertson; James Boswell; and the Hon. Henry Erskine.

(b) *View of the High Street of Edinburgh and the Commissioner going to the General Assembly of the Kirk of Scotland in 1793.* Here again Allan's pre-occupation with religious ceremonies is evident. The long procession winding up the High Street, the State coaches, the church dignitaries in their court dresses, and the military escort combine to impress one with the importance and dignity of this great annual event in the life of the community. This sketch can be compared with Skene's water colour drawing of a similar scene.

(c) *The High Street before the removal of the Luckenbooths.* An aquatint dated 1793. This print is of particular interest for its studies of the contemporary life of the streets. The narrowing of the High Street by the Luckenbooths and the old tower of St. Giles are prominent features. The town crier, chimney sweeps, water caddies, sedan chair carriers and numerous other characters fill the foreground, giving life and movement to the drawing. The trade signs are quaint—Kiniburgh, Glasier; W. Culbertson, Sadlery Warehouse; The Damask Wares Room; and Legs, Arms, and Snuffbox made and sold by Gav. W. [Wilson] Shoemaker. It was this type of picture which earned for Allan the soubriquet ' the Scottish Hogarth.' Alexander Campbell in his *Journey from Edinburgh,* published in 1811, remarks on this characteristic of Allan's works in these terms:—

> " Allan, the late drawing master of the school in the University of Edinburgh, was perhaps the most successful painter of the character and manners of the Scottish peasantry that ever attempted this style of painting. . . .
>
> His works in aquatinto are well known; but his comic sketches are his best productions. A fond admirer would think them hardly inferior to those of Teniers or of Hogarth."

Though most art critics would hesitate to endorse the latter part of that statement nowadays there is no doubt that the work of Allan in this respect was particularly notable.

(d) *The Ceremony of Laying the Foundation Stone of the New College of Edinburgh, November 16, 1789.* This etching is a lively presentation of a great occasion in the educational life of the City. The artist's eye has caught the spirit of the day and the grouping of the Provost, Magistrates, and Council, Professors, and other officials watching the ceremony lend a sense of dignity and civic pride to the occasion. The great crowd assembled along the route; boys clambering over the housetops to get the best viewpoints; an irascible female quarrelling with two soldiers controlling the crowd; and other humorous touches combine to make a picturesque and striking composition.

These four prints are valuable pictorial records of important historical events in the life of the City and Allan's artistic perception of the need for recording them has placed future research workers greatly in his debt.

Allan was also interested in the lighter side of life. This is illustrated by the engraving of the original diploma which he did for the Honourable Company of Edinburgh Golfers. It takes the form of an oval vignette showing a golfer of the period driving from the tee, with a view of Edinburgh Castle in the background. The player is dressed in knee breeches and wears a wide-brimmed hat, while he swings energetically his old-fashioned club. The print is now rare but it is a beautiful piece of work. It was done in 1787 and is reproduced in volume 18 of the *Book of the Old Edinburgh Club*.

The Royal Burgess Society, Barnton, possesses a characteristic sketch by Allan of the Silver Club competition. Intimation of the day on which the competition was due to be played was made by tuck of drum, a unique ceremony for such a purpose. The leader of the procession in resplendent uniform proudly carried a driver festooned with golf balls tied on with coloured ribbons. This sketch was done in 1787. A reproduction of it is in the Edinburgh Room.

Other sketches by Allan such as *Scotch Wedding* and *The Repentance Stool* are reminiscent of the work of his successor Sir David Wilkie, who was noted for his drawings and paintings of the homely scenes and incidents of every-day Scottish life.

Contemporary with Allan we have John Clerk of Eldin whose etchings have earned for him a place as one of the pioneers of the art. E. S. Lumsden in volume 12 of the *Print Collector's Quarterly* says that "Clerk attained to an extraordinary technical proficiency in etching proper, particularly in the long series of plates hardly larger than a visiting card. Of these *Sherriff Hall* and *Lauriston Castle* are two of the finest." But he also did medium sized and indeed quite large plates. His views of *Craigmillar Castle, The Hill of Arthur's Seat, Edinburgh from Lochend, Picardy near Edinburgh,* and *Edinburgh, Salisbury Craigs,* and the *Wrytes Houses* all show that he could work on a larger scale when he wished. Outwith the City he etched a very fine view of *Durham Cathedral,* and on the immediate fringes of the town he found material in the old castles of Borthwick, Crichton, Dalhousie, and Melville for his graver. These same fringes provided him with the background for his beautiful sketches *Dalkeith from the North West,* and

Clerk

Hillhead, near Lasswade, both notable for their superb treatment of trees and country landscapes, and for a softness of tone which is also most noticeable in the *Craigmillar* etching illustrated here.

The Lochend print noted above illustrates wild duck shooting over the Loch and also gives a picture of Lochend House on the high ground to the left overlooking the water. Of quite a different type, the view of the mansion of Wrytes Houses from the south west exhibits an imposing array of gables. Cockburn's *Memorials* (illustrated edition) reproduces this view and provides various references to that famous building.

Another of Clerk's larger sketches is *The Old Church of St. Cuthbert and North Loch,* a lithographic reproduction of which by Schenck and McFarlane is well known. Grant used it as the frontispiece of volume 1 of his *Old and New Edinburgh.* This is probably the best available view of the Loch, the Well House Tower, the broad path by the waterside, and the Church with its quaint spire.

Clerk was much interested in the sea and his treatise on naval tactics was an astounding work for a layman. This interest is reflected in his *Leith from the West,* a medium sized view of the old Tower, the breakwater, and the smoking kilns of the glass works in the background. In the Port he found scope for depicting the sailing ships, fishing vessels and harbour scenes which had always fascinated him.

Clerk etched about 90 plates of which the Bannatyne Club brought together 28 in a large folio volume issued by the Club in 1825. This was to have contained biographical matter about Eldin and also descriptive notes of each of his etchings. These were omitted, but some years later Clerk's son discovered many other etchings in an old cupboard drawer. The Club issued a second volume in 1855, this time with all the notes and a fine portrait after Sir Henry Raeburn engraved by Schenck and Mcfarlane.

Paul Sandby and Clerk were great friends and indeed it is said that Sandby taught Clerk etching. Furthermore it is of particular interest to note that Mr. Martin Hardie, R.E., contributed two letters to the *Print Collector's Quarterly* (volume 20, 1933) which prove conclusively that Sandby gave Clerk details of the then new aquatint process with which he was experimenting. Sandby was thrilled with the new method of reproduction which he was to use later with great success.

Lumsden asserts that Clerk was influenced by foreign engravers and certainly some of his plates show a measure of kinship to Hollar's work.

PLATE 13

CRAIGMILLAR CASTLE
Etching by J. Clerk of Eldin. 1777

PLATE 14

EDINBURGH FROM THE SOUTH-EAST

Engraving by R. Scott after A. Carse. 1801

PLATE 15

EDINBURGH CASTLE FROM THE GRASSMARKET
Coloured aquatint by F. Nicholson. c. 1810

APPROACH TO THE CALTON HILL

Coloured aquatint by R. Scott after R. Crichton. 1814

PLATE 16

He pays tribute to this noted craftsman in these terms :—

" Historically, Clerk must take a definite, and not unimportant place
as a pioneer in this country. He has individuality, and the records
of his neighbourhood are unmistakably of the soil, a quality only
arrived at when the etcher really loves his subject and is also a
genuine artist, though not necessarily an accomplished one. Some
few of his finest plates entitle him to a definite and permanent
place among the etchers who count."

Alexander Nasmyth was born in Edinburgh in 1758. He went to
London and became a pupil of Allan Ramsay. Later he departed for
Rome where he spent several years. Though he is now best known by
his famous portrait of Robert Burns it must not be forgotten that he
executed many fine landscapes, and not a few of them of Edinburgh
scenes. Several engraved copies of these are in the Library collection.
One of the most pleasing is his *Edinburgh from the Glasgow Road,* a
coloured engraving by J. Hollis done in 1821. This lovely view from
the west has a most picturesque foreground, a rural scene with trees,
a stage coach, and figures, forming a fine contrast to the Castle,
Heriot's, and other notable places seen in the distance.

Nasmyth was also responsible for an extraordinary sketch for the
proposed Monument to be erected on the Calton Hill in memory of the
gallant Nelson. Actually it was never erected, wisely one must admit.
The base of the Monument, rising from a precipitous and rocky bluff,
represents nothing so much as a western pioneer's shack—hardly
in keeping with the naval symbols above the inscribed plaque. The
Admiral's victories of Trafalgar, Copenhagen, and the Nile are com-
memorated by great bands round the tall tapering column on the hillside.
The artist did another view of the same intended Monument as it would
appear from Princes Street. Both sketches are dated 1806 and were
engraved by R. Scott.

A photographic reproduction of Nasmyth's picture of Edinburgh
from Hanover Street, looking east, showing the Royal Institution under
construction, is unfortunately all that the Library possesses of this
magnificent painting. The reproduction is a large one measuring
18.9 inches by 14. It shows Princes Street crowded with people, and
workmen busy on the great pillars of Playfair's classical structure.

Nasmyth also published sixteen views of the places mentioned in
the Waverley Novels. These were done in the form of vignettes and

engraved by W. H. Lizars. Six of them relate to Edinburgh, chiefly because of the *Heart of Midlothian* interest.

Macpherson   In 1789 there was published a collection of engravings entitled *Edina Delineata*; or picturesque perspective views of the public and remarkable buildings, &c. in the City of Edinburgh and its environs. With an account, descriptive and historic, accompanying each view. Designed, drawn, engraved, and written by Aeneas Macpherson. The work was issued in four paper covered parts each containing four views. As far as I have been able to ascertain only the first part had the descriptive notes but the author assures us that " the whole was calculated to lead to an adequate conception of this ancient and flourishing metropolis and its environs." The artist lives up to his rather egotistical advertisement for the plates are competent examples of the engraver's craft though without other outstanding merit. They are as undernoted:—

Part 1. Holyrood Palace; St. Anthony's Chapel; The North Bridge; Register Office.

Part 2. St. Roque's Chapel; Hume's Tomb; Castle and St. Cuthbert's Church.

Part 3. Ruins of Holyrood Chapel; The New Bridewell; N.W. View of Heriot's Hospital; High Street from the Tron Church.

Part 4. St. George's Chapel; Episcopal Chapel, Cowgate; and St. Andrew's Church; Trinity College Church; Royal Infirmary and Royal Exchange; Parliament House.

5

PRINTS OF THE 19th CENTURY

In the first part of the 19th century the Scott family were the Scott family leading figures in the Edinburgh engraving world. The father, Robert, lived from 1777-1841 and according to Bryan he was the " best Scottish engraver of his time." Certainly he and his sons occupied a prominent place in the artistic life of the City.

Robert was born in Lanark and at an early age he was apprenticed to A. Robertson (mentioned on page 18) from whom he learned the rudiments of engraving. No fewer than 34 of his works are in the Edinburgh Room collection, all of local subjects. His business was located on Parliament Stairs where he employed many assistants, mostly on book illustration. He himself was responsible for the plates for James Anderson's *The Bee* and in 1795-6 he engraved *Views of Seats and Scenery chiefly in the Environs of Edinburgh,* from drawings by A. Carse and A. Wilson. Then in 1801 he produced a very fine plate entitled *Edinburgh from the South-East* also after A. Carse. Dedicated to the Lord Provost, this fine print takes a familiar viewpoint. In the foreground are the ruins of St. Anthony's Chapel with cattle browsing on the hillside. Further on a lady and gentleman are strolling with their small son who is absorbed with his bow and arrow, and a shepherd is seen carrying a sheep on his back. The South Back of the Canongate on the left, slopes down to Holyrood and Clockmill House, the middle is filled in with the great ridge to the Castle, and on the right is the Calton Hill with its monuments.

In 1814 Scott did a fine coloured aquatint entitled *Elevation of the Approach to the Calton Hill by Wellington Bridge,* after R. Crichton which illustrates the east end of Princes Street with the portico of the Theatre Royal on the right, part of the Register House on the left, and straight ahead the Nelson Monument with the Grecian pillars of the High School below. Artistic licence has come into play here for it is not possible to see the school from this viewpoint.

Another aspect of the same district appears in Scott's print *Effect from Princes Street of the intended monument on the Calton Hill in memory of the gallant Nelson* from a drawing by A. Nasmyth, which was used as an illustration in the *Scots Magazine* for 1806. Three years later he did a large tinted engraving entitled *Monument to the memory of Lord Nelson, erected on the Calton Hill, Edinburgh* from a drawing by R. Burn, the architect. Measuring 10.5 inches by 16.6 this is a particularly fine piece of work which transmits to posterity the fame of the victor of Trafalgar.

Like David Allan, Scott did a whole series of engravings for Ramsay's *Gentle Shepherd,* in this instance for the edition of 1808. These were after A. Carse and J. Stevenson, and took the form of views of the localities referred to in Ramsay's great pastoral. Nine of these engravings were published in the *Edinburgh Magazine* for 1801-3 accompanied by descriptions of the landscapes.

Scott's prolific graver kept him fully employed in supplying views for the *Scots Magazine,* a large number of which represented Edinburgh scenes. Though small in size they were quite attractive. He also engraved maps, sometimes with views inset, such as those incorporated in *The Strangers Guide . . . to Edinburgh and Leith* issued in 1805.

A number of plates from drawings by A. Wilson for *Twelve Views in the Vicinity of the Metropolis of Scotland, 1801* were engraved by Scott. Five Edinburgh items appeared in the volume—*Edinburgh from the North-West* and *Duddingston House* engraved by Wilson himself, and *Bellevue, Hermitage of Braid,* and *Craigiehall Bridge* engraved by A. Carse. In this instance Scott worked on the places outwith the City. Useful historical notes on the places illustrated were contributed by Robert Heron, who is well known as the author of several books on Scotland.

In 1838 Scott's son, W. B., produced a set of drawings which were published in book form by W. F. Watson, 52 Princes Street, under the title *Scenery of Edinburgh & Midlothian.* The volume had forty-two preliminary pages of descriptive text to introduce the twenty views for which his father did the engraving. The Edinburgh plates were :—

Edinburgh from the Pentlands.
Craigmillar Castle.
Hunters Bog.

North Bridge.

Portobello, showing Leith Citadel and Portobello Tower.

Statue of George IV.

Edinburgh from the Cat Nick.

Burns' Monument.

Parliament House. An animated scene showing lawyers in wigs and gowns striding about in the great hall, with its magnificent ceiling and great stained glass window.

Leith; showing the Signal Tower, pier, breakwater, sailing ships, fishing smacks, etc.

Duddingston in winter with skaters on the Loch.

Castlehill.

In these pages Scott stresses the changing scene—the gradual sweeping away of familiar landmarks, the disappearance of the convivial howffs of former times, and even the abandonment of Leith Links for Bruntsfield and Barnton as recreational spots.

William Bell Scott contributed little more of importance to the topographical aspect of Edinburgh than the sketches noted above, but notices of his artistic and poetic circle of friends are given in a volume edited by W. Minto in 1892.

The other son, David, is best known by his great picture of Vasco da Gama encountering the Spirit of the Storm as he passes the Cape of Good Hope, now hung in Trinity House, Leith.

The Lizars family had a long and noteworthy connection with Lizars family engraving in Edinburgh. Daniel lived from 1760-1812. He was a pupil of Andrew Bell already mentioned. Six of his engravings are mentioned in *The Edinburgh Scene,* the most important of which is the *View of the New Bridge of Edinburgh,* with the adjacent buildings of the old and new town, from the west, dated about 1775 and measuring 11.5 inches by 6.7. Another interesting item is the *Perspective View of South Bridge Street and the adjacent buildings, according to the intended plan,* which appeared in the *Edinburgh Magazine* for 1786. This illustrates the narrow thoroughfare before the two bays of the Tron Church were removed to provide the additional width for the new development. It also shows the old wooden steeple of the church.

Daniel's son, William Home Lizars, was one of the great figures in the Edinburgh engraving world and he also achieved a considerable measure of success as a painter. On the death of his father, however, he had to cast aside his easel and palette in order to support his mother and her large family. As an engraver he accomplished much fine work and the name of Lizars on illustrative material was a guarantee of competent craftsmanship. Most of the 30 specimens of his work in the Library stock are small and of well known subjects in the City but his *View of the junction of Leopold Place with Hillside Crescent, taken from the Great London Road* is an etching from an unusual viewpoint.

Like many other engravers William experimented with new methods of reproduction and he is said to have perfected an etching process which performed all the functions of wood engraving in connection with the illustration of books. A series of 26 plates of Natural History —birds and animals—beautifully engraved in colour is a characteristic example of his experimental work.

As a family business, sometimes designated W. & D. and sometimes W. H. & D., the firm was responsible for much engraved work, including a *Design for the National Monument of Scotland* for which A. Elliot, architect, had conceived the plan. This was a magnificent domed conception which was abandoned—another of Edinburgh's discarded projects. The building was approached by a great flight of steps above which rose two storeys of pillared columns, one above the other, and then over all the great dome itself. The design is classical throughout. The ground plan for the *Design* shows a portico, inscription hall and church with colonnades.

Caldwall   In 1799 J. Caldwall did a fine aquatint entitled *View of the City of Edinburgh* after Adam Callender. The Library copy is a signed proof dedicated in manuscript to the Earl of Hardwicke. The viewpoint is Arthur's Seat, with the Calton Hill and the South Back of the Canongate on the extreme right and left, and the solid mass of City buildings towering up towards the Castle. Jacob's Ladder is shown but Regent Terrace and Royal Circus have no place as they were not constructed until later. Leith and the Forth are lightly touched in. The print is done in pale blues and greens. The houses of the Old Town show no architectural refinements and the general effect is rather formal. The same remark applies to the new bridge and its three great arches which form a central feature of the print. Soldiers are drilling on the parade ground to the east of Holyrood, a happy touch which livens up the composition.

John Stoddart's *Remarks on Local Scenery and Manners in Scotland* Stoddart *during . . . 1799 and 1800* contains four items relating to Edinburgh. The first is a vignette of St. Bernard's Well, engraved by W. Poole, on the title-page. The others are three fine aquatints, two of them drawn by J. C. Nattes and engraved by J. Merigot, and the third sketched by Grecian Williams and also engraved by Merigot.

The first is Edinburgh Castle from the foot of the West Port. The towering bulk of the fortress stands firm and commanding above the quaint old buildings at the western end of the Grassmarket. The second represents the Castle from the west with a most pleasing aspect of Heriot's Hospital on the right. The heavy mass of the Castle is lightened by the distance, while the agricultural operations going on in the foreground are in keeping with the general surroundings. The third aquatint depicts the limestone quarry at Gilmerton colourfully treated—an interesting print on a small scale. Curiously enough this quarry attracted a number of other artists including Nattes and James Skene.

John Claude Nattes, an English artist, was commissioned to do the Nattes drawings for a work entitled *Scotia Depicta* which would illustrate and describe old castles, notable antiquities, and the seats of gentlemen and noblemen worthy of inclusion in the volume. For the work he did the undernoted etchings of Edinburgh :—

> Edinburgh. 1804.
> Gilmerton Quarry. 1799.
> Edinburgh Castle from the Vennel. 1800.
> St. Bernard's Well. 1799.
> Register Office. 1804.

All were engraved by J. Fittler, a noted London artist who specialised in line engraving and was well known for the high quality of his book illustrations. The last item is badly titled as only a very small part of the Register House appears to the right of the print, and the Castle, the Princess Street Coffee House with Pool's Hotel above it, and the view along the street are the main features.

In 1801 Nattes executed two very pleasing sketches of Edinburgh Castle—one from the foot of the West Port and the other from the west.

These small, but nevertheless attractive aquatints, were done by J. Merigot, an engraver of whom comparatively little is known.

A topographical collection of some artistic merit entitled *An Elegant Collection of Interesting Views in Scotland,* representing gentlemen's seats, remains of places of antiquity, and picturesque scenery, accurately and neatly engraved, accompanied with suitable descriptions, appeared 'in 1802. It was issued in thirteen sets with six views in each part; printed by Oliver & Co., Netherbow, and published by Reid & Scott, Booksellers, opposite the College, South Bridge Street.

The views originally appeared in the *Edinburgh Magazine* or *Literary Miscellany* between 1785 and 1800. Many Edinburgh places are included :—

> Set 1. Abbey and Palace of Holyrood House; Ruins of the Chapel of Holyrood House; Herriot's Hospital; Craigmillar Castle; St. Bernard's Well; University of Edinburgh.
>
> Set 2. Hermitage of Braid; Edinburgh Bridewell; Edinburgh Castle; Restalrig Church.
>
> Set 3. Wrytes Houses; Inch House; Craig Crook.
>
> Set 4. Lawrieston Castle; Collington House; Spylaw.

The other sets contain no Edinburgh items. Six of the prints were engraved by A. Robertson and two by R. Scott after drawings by F. Dick, James Denholm and others. They measured approximately 6½ inches by 4, and though they vary in quality they are neat and skilfully executed.

Carr   In 1809 Sir John Carr did an unusual aquatint entitled *Edinburgh from the West* which illustrates strikingly the valley where later Princes Street Gardens were laid out. The bed of the North Loch, now drained and levelled up, is flanked on the right by the massive proportions of the Bank of Scotland, while in the middle distance the North Bridge is the outstanding feature. The aquatint was used as the frontispiece of Sir John's *Caledonian Sketches* in which there appears that witty comment on George Street which was at that time the master-piece of the New Town. " George's Street is very fine: the people of Edinburgh think it injured by what is whimsically called the *impudence* of the clergy in bringing the church of St. Andrew so far forward, and the *modesty* of the physicians in placing their hall so far back."

Ibbetson   Another interesting print of this year is J. C. Ibbetson's sketch,

PLATE 17

VIEW OF THE OLD TOWN OF EDINBURGH
Coloured aquatint by J. Clark after A. Kay. 1814

PLATE 18

VIEW OF THE OLD TOWN TAKEN FROM CLARKE'S CIRCULATING LIBRARY
Coloured aquatint by J. Clark after A. Kay. 1812

PLATE 19

GEORGE HERIOT'S HOSPITAL FROM THE CASTLE HILL
Engraving by W. H. Lizars after J. Ewbank. 1825

PLATE 20

Princes Street from the Calton Hill during George IV's Reign
Engraving by W. H. Lizars after J. Ewbank. 1825

Edinburgh from the Calton Hill, engraved in aquatint by R. G. Reeve. It is a large engraving measuring 23 inches by 17. Reeve was noted for his sporting prints done during the first half of the nineteenth century, but this departure from his more usual artistic field indicates his versatility. The print gives a straight view along Princes Street and illustrates the regularity and compactness of the buildings at this period. The dome and small side towers of the Register House, the graceful spire of St. Andrew's Church, the North Bridge, Hume's Monument, and St. Giles, all come into the picture. The Library possesses two copies, one in black and white, the other in colour.

A further example of Ibbetson's work is in the collection—an undated but very fine water colour of St. Bernard's Well in which the classical features of the structure are admirably brought out.

A coloured aquatint by F. J. Sargent done in 1810 is a print much sought after by collectors and consequently highly priced. Rather formal in style, the engraver has indicated important places by titles at the foot of the print—Bank, Old Town, Princes Street, etc. It is interesting to see the pinnacled roof of Trinity College Church well below the Bridewell and the jumble of houses which at that period formed Shakespeare Square. The newly formed Mound is a prominent feature with the West Church in the distance. Stage coaches and family conveyances jog along Princes Street and across the North Bridge. *Sargent*

Three of the finest aquatints in the collection were executed by J. Clark. Two of them are after A. Kay. They are :— *Clark*

View of the Old Town, taken from Clarke's Circulating Library, South St. Andrew Street. 1812.

Salisbury Crags, the spire of the Tron Church, and the crown of St. Giles silhouetted against a stormy sky. In the centre of the picture are the Canal Street buildings on the site now taken up by the railway and the Waverley Market, and to the right of them the Little Mound, now the Waverley Bridge. The scene is enlivened by the stage coach swinging along Princes Street, with others parked on the south side awaiting passengers, and the fashionably dressed strollers on the sidewalk.

A most interesting variant of this print is dated 1814. In this case the engraving extends a little further to the east and shows a part of the Theatre Royal.

View of the Old Town taken from Princes Street. 1814.

The Bank of Scotland, Ramsay Gardens, and the Castle form an attractive background. No classical structures have yet been erected on the Earthen Mound which spans what remains of the Nor' Loch, while away to the extreme right the spire of the West Church can just be seen. A picturesque phaeton and pair, a gentleman on horseback, and figures in period costume complete the foreground of this most attractive print.

Clark's third aquatint is his *City of Edinburgh.* It measures 21.8 inches by 14.8 and is dated 1824. The view is from the north west. In the foreground beautiful trees grace the park lands and the Castle, Heriot's, and St. George's Church also come into the picture. A group of ladies and gentlemen lazing about add a lively touch to the scene. The Calton Hill, Nelson Monument, and Arthur's Seat complete a beautiful soft toned composition.

Gibson   Patrick Gibson, an Edinburgh landscape painter and etcher, issued in 1818 six etchings of *Select Views in Edinburgh* consisting chiefly of prospects that have presented themselves, and public buildings that have been erected in the course of the recent improvements of the City. Accompanied by historical and explanatory notices the etchings are :—

1. Regent Bridge, New Jail, etc. from the west.
2. Princes Street from Regent Bridge.
3. Edinburgh Castle from the Grassmarket.
4. Old Jail or Tolbooth, County-Hall, and St. Giles Church.
5. The Weigh House.
6. Interior of the Chapel of Holy-Rood House from the west.

The plates measure roughly 9 inches by 7 but they vary in that respect and the last is a double one of 17 inches by 12. The first three etchings show construction operations in progress and are very interesting for that reason, particularly as they are very clearly numbered for identification purposes. Gibson also did a nice sketch entitled *View of Edinburgh (from the Calton Hill)* which was engraved by G. Cooke in 1809. He himself was a pupil of A. Nasmyth and later he had some part in training Geikie in his artistic work. He lived from 1782-1829 and at various times he occupied 23 Dundas Street and 15 Elder Street.

A. Carse, who lived during the first half of the 19th century, was Carse responsible for various sketches illustrating scenes from the domestic life of the Scottish people, and like Geikie, he frequently introduced touches of humour in his drawings. To his friends and acquaintances he was familiarly known as ' Old Carse ' and Cockburn in his *Memorials* has this to say of him. " Some pretended to call him the Teniers of Scotland; a title by the help of which he excited attention, and some hope. But, though he certainly had humour, I doubt if he would ever have got the better of his coarseness and bad training, both in drawing and colouring." That judgment would appear a trifle severe in view of the neat and competent sketches he did in collaboration with his colleague A. Wilson, and which, as I have already indicated, were very skilfully engraved by that noted artist Robert Scott. His chief topographic achievement was his *Edinburgh from the South East,* a large sketch measuring 16.1 inches by 11.1 which Scott also engraved in most attractive fashion. Of this the Library possesses a very fine copy in colour as well as the original print. His drawings of Craigiehall Bridge and of Leith Races are also worthy of note.

One of Edinburgh's greatest engravers was Robert Kirkwood who Kirkwood is best known for his map of 1817. But in 1819 he issued from his place of business in Parliament Square an unusual combination of plan and view. The area covered is from Canonmills Loch to Canal Street, and from Melville Street to Gayfield Square. The unique feature of this remarkable specimen of the engraver's art is the manner in which the whole of the New Town, with the elevations of the streets and buildings, is depicted in pictorial form. Charlotte Square and St. Andrew's Square are shown with a fine elevation of St. George's Church in the one case and the Excise Office in the other, while at the east end of George Street the frontage of St. Andrew's Church with its slim spire is exquisitely engraved. Lest it should be thought that the scene is dominated by the ecclesiastical background it must be mentioned that a careful scrutiny leads the eye to that depressing Trinity—the Debtor's Jail, the Bridewell, and the Felon's Jail. Nearby is the façade of the Theatre Royal in Shakespeare Square.

The print also shows St. John's Chapel and the West Church, the latter with its great range of burial vaults adjacent. The North Loch and the Earthen Mound are still in the picture and Canal Street is a conglomeration of dwelling houses, timber and coach yards, and other curiously assorted buildings. Further north the Village of Broughton is nicely laid out and other places too numerous to mention here are most meticulously set down. The reference value of the view is greatly enhanced by the fact that all the buildings in the streets are numbered while in many cases the owners of the properties are given.

Kirkwood also issued on a smaller scale a *Specimen of a Proposed Plan and Elevation of the Old Town of Edinburgh* which was to be on similar lines, but it came to naught. A reduced print of this was distributed to advertise the new project and a copy of it is in the Edinburgh Room. He was also responsible for a re-engraved copy of the 1582 view of Braun and Hogenberg and a reproduction of Gordon of Rothiemay's bird's-eye view of 1647, both of which were issued in 1817.

Paterson

About this time Daniel Macintosh, Repository of the Arts, St. Andrew's Street, issued *Twelve Etchings of Views in Edinburgh, by an amateur, 1816.* The anonymous etcher was William Paterson who dedicated his work to Sir Walter Scott. The plates are of sufficient merit to warrant a fuller designation on the title-page more in keeping with the quality of the work, for the illustrations are well chosen and skilfully executed though not of the highest quality. The subjects are as follows :—

1. Residence of the Archbishop of St. Andrews
2. View in the Cowgate
3. Church and Hospital of St. Mary Magdalen
4. Church of Mary de Gueldres. An unusual view showing the position of the old houses built against the west wall
5. View at foot of Leith Wynd
6. Monastery of the Holy Cross, or Holyrood
7. East view of Heriot's Hospital
8. Heriot's Hospital from the Grey Friars
9. View near the Fountain-Well, High Street. John Knox is seen at a window of his house haranguing a small band of rather bored looking spectators
10. Ancient Assembly Rooms, West Bow
11. St. Giles
12. Edinburgh Castle, from the south

Each view has a descriptive page of letterpress describing prominent features of the etching.

Paterson's venture proved successful and the favourable reception given to the initial part encouraged him to proceed with a continuation which was published in the same year, this time by Archibald Constable. It is in exactly the same format and style as the original volume and the numbered plates are listed here :—

13. Holyrood House and Abbey, from the Calton Hill
14. Tolbooth and Linen-Hall, Canongate
15. Trinity College Church, from the east
16. Monuments of Hume, Lord Nelson, etc.
17. Drummond's Land, Cowgate
18. Old Houses opposite College Wynd, Cowgate. Showing Weaver's Land and Pott's Land, typical examples of the house frontages said to have been constructed from timber cut down on the Borough Muir. The location is clearly defined by the shop sign of Andrew Craig, spirit dealer at 174 Cowgate.
19. Heriot's Hospital, from the West Bow
20. Hospital of St. Mary Magdalene and Church of St. Giles
21. Tombs of Mr. Adam, Dr. Robertson, etc.
22. View of Cross Causeway
23. View at the West Port
24. Edinburgh Tolbooth and the Church of St. Giles

A companion volume entitled *Scenery and Antiquities of Midlothian* appeared in 1819. Certain of the places covered in the volume are now within the City boundaries. They are :—

1. Edinburgh and its environs—from the Fife coast, a little to the east of Fordel House. Inset a view of the ruined Restalrig Church.
2. View from Corstorphine Hill
3. View from Stockbridge. Shows buildings being erected in the grounds of Raeburn, the portrait painter. Above the tree embowered slopes of the background can be seen the dome of the new St. George's Church.

4. St. Anthony's Chapel
5. Merchiston Tower. The Tower was used as a prison by Drury, the English General who led the southern forces to the assistance of the Earl of Morton, the Regent. At the time when the drawing was made the apartment in which Napier compiled his Tables of Logarithms was still intact in its original state.
6. Craigmillar Castle

The remaining etchings lie outwith the scope of this monograph.

Daniel Macintosh, the publisher of Paterson's etchings, issued a particularly fine trade card advertising his wares. His place of business was then at 49 Princes Street. Macintosh was an English and foreign print seller and also a carver and gilder, while his other activities included the supply of Ladies' Fancy Works (whatever these might be), stationery, water colours, and all requisites for drawing. The card also informs the public that "Drawing is taught and drawings and prints lent to copy."

The card shows a lovely bow-fronted window on the street level, with five doorways on either side and artistic balconies above. It is a fine piece of engraving. The shop frontage is clearly shown in Ebsworth's northern view from the Scott Monument, mention of which is made elsewhere.

Thomson   A noted Scottish artist during the early years of the 19th century was the Rev. John Thomson, minister of Duddingston, who earned for himself a reputation far beyond his native land. He did two paintings of Craigmillar Castle which were engraved by W. Woolnoth and J. C. Allen in 1820 and 1835 respectively. The Woolnoth engraving shows the castle walls and turrets above the trees to the right and a great stretch of rural landscape to the left. Allen's plate on the other hand presents a much fuller view of the castle with trees and some figures in the foreground.

Another drawing, *Edinburgh from Corstorphin Hill,* was also engraved by Woolnoth. It is dated 1819 and is a masterly interpretation of the scenic panorama between the hill and the dominating rock which overshadows the distant prospect of all views from the west.

These three pictures were engraved for the *Provincial Antiquities of Scotland* by Sir Walter Scott. They are typical examples of Thomson's ability to put on canvas the characteristics and atmosphere of Scottish scenery. Thomson was a close personal friend of Sir Walter and at one time he was considered in connection with the illustration of a collected edition of Scott's works but ultimately Turner was commissioned to provide the drawings.

One of the striking prints in the collection shows the *first George* Masson *Watson's Hospital,* drawn by A. S. Masson, then a mere lad of 13 years of age. It is a wonderfully mature piece of work. The school was taken over by the Royal Infirmary about 1879. The drawing, which measures 17 inches by 10.8, was engraved by R. Scott and issued in 1819. It can undoubtedly be reckoned one of the engraver's best efforts. The sketch is quite a lively composition with pupils practising archery in the playground, others kite flying, and parents strolling amongst the boys.

Masson also drew a sketch entitled *Leith from the Pier,* which was engraved by J. Gellatly. This is a much less pretentious effort but, as it is undated, one can hardly compare it with the Watsonian print. It has the appearance, however, of being a much later piece of work.

The name of Daniel Somerville is one which must not be over- Somerville looked in the art life of the City during the early part of the 19th century. He was a line engraver who did some fine book illustrations and topographical plates, while his pencil sketches of Edinburgh scenes were executed with meticulous care. In 1817 he sent out his *Sixteen Original Sketches of Edinburgh* and followed that up with *Thirty Drawings* in 1826. Done in careful detail these pencil sketches of Edinburgh bye-ways are most picturesque. Sir Daniel Wilson found them so attractive that he used them while he was preparing his *Memorials of Edinburgh* for he realised that the places depicted had, in many cases, been swept away by the planners of the newer " Auld Reekie." In addition to the publications noted above there are twenty-six separate items in the collection, including water colours, etchings, and lithographs.

Somerville was an experimenter in the lithographic art as this reference from the *Print Collector's Quarterly* of 1934 shows :—

A Sketch from a Mutilated Bass [*Sic*] *Relief:* drawn and executed on marble, by corroding away the lights surrounding the lines, and printed on the surface in the manner of the Letterpress Prints of the Early Engravers. By Daniel Somerville. Edin. 1818.

" That the Edinburgh artists considered Somerville's exhibits of importance may be gathered from the fact that whereas descriptions of the works of the great majority of exhibitors are accorded a line apiece, here we have Somerville occupying a whole page. Yet Somerville's name and the inventions to which he lays claim seem to have been omitted from the records of the art of lithography."

Several of Somerville's copperplates are exhibited in Lady Stair's House in the Lawnmarket.

Storer   This period was very prolific insofar as the production of prints was concerned and in 1820 a collection of engraved views was issued by J. and H. S. Storer entitled *Views in Edinburgh and its Vicinity*. The publishers were A. Constable and Co. A lengthy preface on the history of the City serves as a useful introduction to the actual prints, which include illustrations of most of the notable edifices of the Capital with appropriate comments on each of the selected items. Among these are buildings of historical significance and also " many new and magnificent structures affording an interesting picture of a city emerging fast from comparative poverty and advancing rapidly to commercial distinction and opulence." Evidently the new planning in these early years of the nineteenth century was something to wonder at, and no doubt it led to much criticism from those who had been accustomed to different conditions. The Storer prints, while of considerable import- ance from a topographic viewpoint, are in themselves a trifle formal and rather lacking in human interest.

There are fully 100 prints in the volumes and some of the state- ments made in the notes attached to each are a trifle unusual. Thus in describing the view of *Hume's Monument from Leith Wynd*, after setting down some biographical information about the noted philosopher and historian, the writer quotes the famous epitaph

> " Within this circular idea
> Called vulgarly a tomb,
> The Impressions and Ideas rest
> That constituted Hume."

Of a different type is the note which accompanies the view of *St. Andrew's Church* anent Henry Erskine's witty remark " that the forwardness of the clergy and the modesty of the physicians had ruined

PLATE 21

St. John's Chapel, Princes Street, from Castle Terrace
Coloured lithograph by Nichol after W. Mason. c. 1845

PLATE 22

MORAY HOUSE

Water colour. Artist unknown. c. 1832

PLATE 23

EDINBURGH FROM THE WEST
Aquatint by Sir J. Carr. 1809

PLATE 24

EDINBURGH CASTLE FROM GRASSMARKET
Pen and wash drawing by W. Geikie. c. 1820

PLATE 25

THE OLD TRON
Pencil drawing by W. Geikie. c. 1820

PLATE 26

OLD EXCISE OFFICE
Etching by Walter Geikie. c. 1829

PLATE 27

STONE QUARRIES, CRAIGLEITH, NEAR EDINBURGH
Engraved by W. Wallis after T. H. Shepherd. 1829

PLATE 28

ST. GEORGE'S CHURCH FROM GEORGE STREET, LOOKING WEST
Engraving by H. W. Bond after T. H. Shepherd. 1829

PLATE 29

High School in 1777

Engraved by J. and H. S. Storer. 1819

PLATE 30

HOLYROOD PALACE

Engraving by W. Byrne and W. Lowry after T. Hearne. 1800

PLATE 31

GREYFRIARS CHURCH

Engraving by T. Steuart after the drawing by Sir Daniel Wilson, 1848

PLATE 32

EDINBURGH CASTLE
Engraving after T. Hearne. 1780

Leith

PLATE 33

LEITH HARBOUR FROM THE PIER
Coloured aquatint by W. Daniell. 1822

the appearance of the finest street in Europe "—another version of the comment on George Street given in Sir John Carr's *Caledonian Sketches* quoted on page 40.

William Daniell, for whose aquatints there is a continuous demand, Daniell did comparatively little to illustrate the beauties of Edinburgh, yet the prints he made are sufficiently interesting to warrant mention here. There are five items, all aquatints, in the Edinburgh Room collection. These are :—

(a) Distant View of Edinburgh, with Wemys Castle. 1822.
(b) Edinburgh from the Calton Hill. 1822.
(c) Edinburgh from the Castle. 1822.
(d) Edinburgh, with part of the North Bridge and Castle. 1822
(e) Leith Harbour from the Pier. 1822.

These prints appeared in the well known *Picturesque Voyage round Great Britain,* issued in eight volumes between the years 1814-25. They all measure approximately 9.5 inches by 6.5. Their delicate tinting and accurate drawing have always been a source of attraction for the eager collector. The Leith Harbour view which is illustrated here is a typical example of his work. The Signal Tower at the end of the harbour wall dominates the left of the picture; in the rear the softly shaded in bulk of Arthur's Seat takes the eye; and in the foreground the calm blue toned water affords a fine contrast for the vessels in the harbour and the brightly dressed figures quietly observing the pleasant scene.

About this time T. M. Baynes was preparing his *Twenty Views of* Baynes *the City and Environs of Edinburgh* which was issued in 1823. Of these, that from the base of the Calton Hill gives a fine impression of the North Bridge and its immediate surroundings. *St. Bernard's Well* is rather peculiar in its imaginative treatment of the Dean Bridge which is not surprising since Telford's famous structure was not completed until 1832. The artist's idea of what the bridge ought to be certainly did not measure up to the conception of the designer. Baynes is much more successful in his picture of the *Half Moon Battery* which is one of the best illustrations of this subject, and quite notable for its fine cloud effects.

These lithographs were printed by C. Hullmandel, himself a fine engraver. Of German origin he was born in 1789. He made many

F   49

improvements in the art of lithography and invented lithotint. He engraved for Cattermole, Stanfield, Haghe, Roberts, and others.

Sutherland   The year 1824 was notable for the issue of four exquisite aquatints by T. Sutherland after J. Gendall as undernoted :—

(a) *Edinburgh from the top of Princes Street.* The churches of St. John and St. Cuthbert fill in the foreground. The buildings on the Mound and the National Monument on Calton Hill had not yet been erected; nor had the widening of Princes Street been carried out as the hollow ground to the left of St. John's clearly shows. The gate on the right is approximately on the site on the Caledonian Hotel. The group of figures seated on the stone wall is a happy touch which adds to the artistic effect of the finished picture.

(b) *Edinburgh from the Calton Hill.* The artist has selected a favourite viewpoint and brings into his picture the mile long stretch of Princes Street with the Castle filling the distant landscape. In the immediate foreground is a bird's eye view of Calton Jail, demolished in 1936 to make way for St. Andrew's House, the administrative headquarters of the Government in Scotland. The grassy slopes of the Hill are in use as a bleaching green.

(c) *Edinburgh from Craigleith Quarry.* Taken from the north west this print gives a rural aspect of the outskirts of the City in striking contrast to those noted above. With the exception of the Castle the other buildings shown in the distance are too far off to have much topographic value, but the print is a very pleasing one, with the Queensferry Road winding through the fields towards the Water of Leith and the Dean.

(d) *Edinburgh from the Castle.* A highly coloured print in which a stormy sky produces a hazy effect in the distance, against which the buildings in the middle foreground are well featured. On the Esplanade a battalion of the garrison is drawn up, and here and there spectators are to be seen watching the manoeuvres. The steeple of St. Giles, the Tron spire, the Bank of Scotland, the North Bridge, and Shakespeare Square buildings are well depicted.

A noted aquatinter in the early 19th century was R. Havell, Jr., Havell who engraved two companion pictures after E. Crawford. The first—*Edinburgh from the Castle*—is a lovely aquatint done in 1828. It is a fine open view over the reclaimed Nor' Loch to Canal Street with the North Bridge, the old Calton Burial Ground, and the Calton Hill with its monuments most effectively used to build up the composition. Soldiers are drilling on the Esplanade and half way down the Mound the Rotunda occupies a prominent position. The view extends down the Forth to Berwick Law which is faintly worked into the background.

The second is *View of Edinburgh from Salisbury Crags* looking up the ridge from Holyrood to Castle, and over to the right to the New Town, Forth, and Fife coast. It was done in 1828.

Havell also engraved a *General View of Edinburgh from the North West* after a drawing by N. A. Kay, dated 1814. It is one of the Whitson Bequest items in Huntly House Museum.

John W. Ewbank was born in Gateshead in 1799, but was long Ewbank resident in Edinburgh where he had a close connection with the Academy. He studied under A. Nasmyth and W. H. Lizars did much of his engraving. An impressive piece of work was his *Picturesque Views of Edinburgh;* the drawings by J. Ewbank, engraved by W. H. Lizars. To which is prefixed, An Historical Sketch of Edinburgh from the earliest to the present times by James Browne, Esq., A.M. 1825. For a young man of 26 this was a wonderful effort and an examination of the separate sketches shows that he was an artist of outstanding ability. The drawings are carefully divided into four groups—distant views, street views (ancient), street views (modern), and miscellaneous views. The most interesting of these 51 sketches are the street scenes, several of them represent viewpoints which have been rarely selected by other artists. The collection is so attractive and uniformly excellent that it is not easy to choose any examples for detailed description, but the two views of the *Lawnmarket and High Street* depicting vividly the stir and bustle of the Capital, and *Edinburgh from Port Hopetoun Union Canal* are particularly worthy of mention, as are also the sketches of *Heriot's Hospital* and *Waterloo Place* illustrated here. The frontispiece of the volume takes the form of a fanciful vignetted view of the Castle and other notable buildings seen through a screen of trees —a most picturesque introduction to a most attractive work. The

Library collection is fortunate in having a complete set of these engravings coloured by hand.

Two large drawings of Ewbank were engraved by W. and A. K. Johnston : *Edinburgh from the Base of Nelson's Monument, Calton Hill*, 1827, and *Edinburgh from the High Battery of the Castle*, 1830. The latter is a view over the North Bridge and out to the Forth and Berwick Law. Castlehill and the heavy block of houses in the Old Town are well shown and a military touch is added by the soldiers drilling on the Esplanade.

In addition to those prints already described Ewbank sketched a view of the City from Inchkeith and also painted the visit of George IV to Edinburgh Castle. Later in life he developed bad habits and a career of great promise ended in 1847.

Callcott   The noted English artist, A. W. Callcott, was commissioned to do some drawings for *The Provincial Antiquities of Scotland,* and three most pleasing engravings of his work are worth noting here. The first is *Castle from the Grassmarket,* a badly titled print for the Castle is but faintly seen above the houses and buildings of the Market itself. The Square is thronged with people—horse copers, water caddies, hucksters, pedlars, and innumerable other types of humanity. A Highland piper plays his Hebridean laments to the accompaniment of snarling dogs. All these details combine to form a lively scene. The second print is *Edinburgh from Braid Hill,* a distant view with the City only lightly sketched in, and a great expanse of country in the foreground. The third scene is *Entrance to Leith Harbour* on a stormy day. Boats of all kinds are reefing sails and seeking the protection of the breakwaters. The engravings were done by H. Le Keux and G. Cooke in 1826.

Burns   In 1829 Matthew Robert Burns issued his *Six Original Lithographic Prints.* Though not of outstanding artistic merit they illustrate some new viewpoints and the notes appended to the lithographs are rather illuminating. The six prints are :—

Covenanters Tomb in Greyfriars.

Old Building, foot of Libberton's Wynd, Cowgate.

West Bow. ' A place full of grandfathers' tales, quite calculated to maintain a Wizard and a Ghost. Both of these it has accordingly done in the person of the notorious Weir, who first served them in the one capacity, and lastly in the other. It is a matter of much regret, that these venerable buildings are very soon to be taken down.'

An Old Building, foot of the High School Wynd, Cowgate. ' According to the information of history, this building was the residence of the Lady of Prince William of Orkney. This celebrated lady was attended by 75 gentle-women, all of whom were attired in silk and velvet, and adorned with chains of gold and valuable jewels. When travelling from Roslin Castle (six miles south of Edinburgh) to the family mansion which was at the foot of this Wynd, she was attended by 200 gentle-men on horseback, and if after night-fall by other 80 persons holding torches.'

Castlehill, Edinburgh.

Regent Murray's Palace, Canongate.

A collection of 120 original drawings by Henry Winkles has been Winkles bound together in a large quarto volume deposited in the Edinburgh Room. The draft title-page states that the sketches were done for his *Views of Edinburgh,* to be published in 1829, along with descriptive notes by Alexander Bower. As far as can be ascertained that work never appeared, for there is no record of the history of the volume between the time when the drawings were done and the date when Mr. Cowan was fortunate enough to acquire them for his collection.

The undernoted drawings are in sepia and alongside the original sketches are the engravings for them :—

St. Anthony's Chapel. The ruin, set on a rocky eminence, appears in striking contrast to the distant view of the Forth.

Royal Institution, Princes Street. A fine impression of Playfair's famous erection with a particularly fine view of the Castle.

John Knox's House. In the sketch the figures are rather poor, but they are altered and improved for the finished engraving.

Melville Monument.

Canongate, Tolbooth.

Regent's Bridge. Two views—one showing the effect in Waterloo Place and the other from the Low Calton.

These sepia sketches are supplemented by 12 pencil sketches of Holyrood, 4 of St. Giles, a considerable number illustrating notable buildings in Leith, and an interesting drawing of the North Bridge from the Nor' Loch before it was completely drained. The Mound embankment is nearing completion. Other items include a sketch of the Bank of Scotland from the Panorama, a specially fine drawing of the City from St. Anthony's Chapel, and an attractive study of Howe Street and St. Stephen's Church.

Geikie   Walter Geikie, that deaf and dumb artistic genius of Edinburgh, was born in 1795 and died in 1837. He went to study under Patrick Gibson and attended the Drawing Academy of the Board of Trustees for the Encouragement of Scottish Manufactures, and his skill was soon appreciated. In spite of his physical disability, or possibly because of it, he worked most assiduously at his self-imposed task of recording the ever-changing life of the streets. His character studies include such subjects as the cobbler at his stall, drunk men, a sea sick dandy, bargaining for fish, and settling for Crummie, the cow. These aspects of the Edinburgh scene place before us a vivid picture of life as it was lived by the poorer classes in those early years of the 19th century, and there was little that his keenly observant eyes missed. Unfortunately he had no gift for colour, and oil painting was beyond his powers. He did, however, many drawings in pencil and wash, but ultimately he found his true métier in etching. David Laing was greatly interested in his work and secured three of his plates for the Bannatyne Club, but only one of them of an Edinburgh subject. This was the west view of the Netherbow Port, almost certainly after Runciman, whose print attracted so many other engravers. These three plates were never used by the Club.

The Broken Pipe, in the Art Department of the Central Library, illustrates his flair for character sketches, some of them with a strong leaning to caricature. On the other hand it must be pointed out that in Bristo Port, Canongate from Abbey Strand, Castle Hill, Crosscauseway showing Buccleuch Church, Edinburgh Castle from the Grassmarket, and The Old Tron—all wash drawings—he illustrates his ability to produce most effectively sketches of a topographic nature. In his street scenes, too, he worked in appropriate local backgrounds to build up the effects he wanted. A volume of 96 original drawings in the Library done round about 1817 deals with such subjects as the West

54

Bow Head, Castlehill, Castle, Blyth's Close, the Grassmarket and St. Anthony's Chapel.

Geikie was fond of working at his easel in St. Luke's Art Club to amuse his friends, and his lightning sketches of the idiosyncracies of many people known to the audience created great hilarity and no doubt helped him to forget his own physical defects.

Geikie did work for H. Paton, a printseller at 21 Horse Wynd. *A Collection of Original Drawings of Edinburgh and Environs* was brought together in 1830, but his memory is permanently enshrined in Sir Thomas Dick Lauder's issue in 1841 of his friend's *Etchings Illustrative of Scottish Character and Scenery; executed after his own designs by the late Walter Geikie, Esq., R.S.A.,* a work which illustrates his reverence for the aged, street vendors and their mannerisms, and Scottish characteristics—domestic interiors, costume, and similar details. In 1885 another edition of these etchings appeared, which inclines one to think that there was a certain justification for the claim that Geikie was the Scottish Rembrandt or at least Van Ostade. The passage of time has, however, somewhat dimmed his reputation and no one would make such a claim now, but undoubtedly he still has a high place in the ranks of Edinburgh artists.

Somewhat later than Geikie Thomas H. Shepherd was engaged on Shepherd a series of drawings measuring approximately 6 inches by 4 each, which were published in 1829 and 1830 under the title *Modern Athens*. The work contained about 100 sketches covering an unusual range of subjects. Few citizens nowadays, for example, could place the "Rainbow" gallery in the engraving of the Fish and Vegetable Market. The drawings were engraved by nineteen different engravers of whom only W. H. Lizars appears to have any Edinburgh connection.

A much more elaborate piece of work engraved by Shepherd was the *View of Edinburgh shewing the communication between the Old and the New Town as proposed by Alexander Trotter, Esqr., of Dreghorn,* 1834. The copy of this fine print in the possession of the Library was presented to the Lord Provost in 1906, and bears the inscription " with Col. P. D. Trotter's compliments." The engraving measures 16.3 inches by 8.9. It illustrates a magnificent thoroughfare on the line of the present day Mound, but sweeping round to the left, and apparently finishing in the neighbourhood of what is now Jeffrey Street. The great advantage of Trotter's proposed improvement lay in the fact that the Princes Street level would have been maintained until the point of entry at the High Street was reached. Trotter's suggestion was undoubtedly a fine conception but apparently it found no favour with the authorities for the project was abandoned. Shepherd's engraving, however, serves as a striking reminder of " what might have been."

Three original water colours of larger size are *Levee room in Regent Murray's House as seen from the garden, Regent Murray's House in the Canongate,* and *West Bow from the Lawnmarket.* These are good examples of his original work and the same may be said of his impressions of Charlotte Square fully one hundred years ago which is illustrated here.

A set of Shepherd's prints in colour is in the Edinburgh Room where it is invaluable for queries relating to early 19th century costume, old horse-drawn carriages, garden railings, lamp-posts of former days, and similar matters.

Batty
About 1830 Lt. Col. Batty painted a number of Edinburgh scenes for a publication entitled *Select Views of the Principal Cities of Europe.* The Edinburgh views are :—

From the Ascent to Arthur's Seat; engraved by W. R. Smith
From the Calton Hill; engraved by G. Cooke
From St. Anthony's Chapel; engraved by W. J. Cooke
From the Calton Hill; engraved by P. H. Hernot
The new Royal High School

All are proof copies in mint state and the Calton Hill item particularly is most attractive with the lively groups of people strolling about in the sunshine. There are kite fliers, sailors, and many other types. This view has a finely drawn key to thirty of the notable points of interest on a separate sheet, and there are other keys which are extremely useful for identification purposes. Each view has descriptive text in French and English.

Batty painted another view which is in the collection—*Edinburgh Castle from the Grassmarket;* engraved by R. Brandard. This is somewhat smaller than the other four but it is in sufficient detail to indicate the names of the proprietors whose businesses come within the scope of the picture. Among these are C. E. Wight, Stabler; Rob Ballantyne, Spirit Dealer; Meal, Barley and Salt Office; Forrest and Hislop, Spirit Dealer; Gladstone, Stabler; Carrier; and James Frier,

PLATE 34

EDINBURGH FROM THE TOP OF PRINCES STREET
Coloured aquatint by T. Sutherland after J. Gendall. 1824.

F**

PLATE 35

EDINBURGH FROM CRAIGLEITH QUARRY
Coloured aquatint by T. Sutherland after J. Gendall. 1824

PLATE 36

EDINBURGH FROM THE CALTON HILL
Coloured aquatint by T. Sutherland after J. Gendall. 1824

PLATE 37

EDINBURGH FROM THE CASTLE, LOOKING EAST
Coloured aquatint by T. Sutherland after J. Gendall. c. 1824

Victualler. The Corn Market with its arched arcading is a typical example of the buildings of the period. Brandard, the engraver, was an artist of high standing who did good work for the Turner Gallery.

William Smeall, a shoemaker who lived from 1790-1883, was Smeall much more devoted to the art of sketching than to his chosen trade, and he contrived to fill two volumes of pencil drawings of old Edinburgh covering a period from about 1815 to 1870. In the catalogue of an Exhibition held in York Place his name appears as an exhibitor in 1815. The sketches have value as records of former scenes done on the spot by one who had a feeling for quaint ' bits ' in and around the City as a large proportion of the drawings are of buildings which have now disappeared. Some of the places depicted lie outwith the City boundaries but the Canongate, Calton, Leith, and the Ports—Potterrow, West Port, Society—are among the places illustrated.

John Petrie, another Edinburgh engraver in the early years of the Petrie century, did six views and two plans for his *Historical Description of the Monastery and Chapel Royal of Holyroodhouse,* published in 1819. The engraving of the artistic outer porch of the Abbey and the plan of the Sanctuary, with its numbered features, are valuable as records of former times. Petrie's name also appears in the *New Picture of Edinburgh of 1816.*

The name of David Roberts ranks high in the artistic roll of fame. Roberts He was born in Church Street, Stockbridge, in 1796 and began his working career as an apprentice to Gavin Beugo, house painter. His itching fingers soon found ready made canvasses on whitewashed walls and other surfaces in the vicinity of his parents' house, and it was early evident that he must somehow or other find an outlet for his artistic talents. Soon he took to scene painting with Corri in Edinburgh and with others elsewhere. About this time he became acquainted with Clarkson Stanfield, another young man who was destined to make his name in the world of art, and they remained friends for life. Cumberland Hill in his *Historic Memorials & Reminiscences of Stockbridge* tells us that Roberts first exhibited three of his drawings in the Exhibition of the Works of Living Artists at Edinburgh in 1822. These were :—

(a) Old Building, Cowgate, Edinburgh.
(b) Interior of New Abbey, Dumfriesshire.
(c) View of the Nether Bow, Edinburgh.

All were sold at the private view and the young artist was greatly encouraged by this early success. After further experience in scene painting at Drury Lane he went abroad to France and Spain. The work accomplished there was much admired on his return to this country and in 1841 he was elected an R.A.

Once more Roberts travelled abroad, on this occasion to Syria and Egypt, where he executed a wonderful gallery of sketches which were issued in four folio volumes under the title, *The Holy Land,* in 1842. These brilliant sketches were finely lithographed by Louis Haghe. They constitute Roberts' greatest artistic achievement.

Four of Roberts' drawings were lithographed on a large scale, roughly 20 inches by 15 each—two by J. D. Harding and two by R. Carrick. They appeared in Lawson's *Scotland Delineated :—*

(a) *Craigmillar Castle.* 1854.

Embowered in trees and in dark shadows Craigmillar is in vivid contrast with Edinburgh Castle which is faintly sketched in. On the right Salisbury Crags and Arthur's Seat are seen with Duddingston Loch and Village sheltering beneath their gentle slopes. This copy is signed by the artist.

(b) *Edinburgh from the Castle.* 1850.

Like the Craigmillar print described above this was also engraved by Harding. The old buildings surrounding the Rotunda near the top of the Mound are conspicuous in the right foreground. They are in deep shadow with which the other parts of the picture contrast strongly. The Scott Monument, the Bank of Scotland, and the North Bridge are important features of the composition. Probably this print gives one of the best representations of the area of the old cattle market, Canal Street, and the great jumble of houses which filled the site now occupied by the North British Hotel and the Waverley Market.

(c) *Edinburgh from Calton Hill.* 1850.

This, the first of the two Carrick lithographs, brings into prominence the Calton Prison and the monuments in the old cemetery adjoining it. Figures resting on the stones and grass on the hillside add to the interest of the scene. Looking along the line of Princes Street one is struck by the fact that as yet there is no National Gallery of Scotland to balance the classical pillars of the Royal Institution.

(d) *Edinburgh from St. Anthony's Chapel.* 1850.
The least interesting of the four lithographs. The artist has introduced a number of figures beneath the walls of the ruined chapel. Holyrood, the Calton Hill monuments, and the Castle come into the picture, while very faintly in the rear appear the dome of St. George's Church and the spire of the Scott Monument.

While these four lithographs are the best examples of his work in the Library the collection also includes three other items worthy of note. These are :—

(a) *Design for Scott Monument.* 1836.
Reproduction of a pencil and wash drawing measuring 8.7 inches by 11.4. The design is a Gothic structure very similar to that of Kemp, but the statue of the novelist is on the very pinnacle of the Monument. An elegant staircase with elaborate balustrading leads to the base, and on the various upper storeys niches, with finely carved representations of the chief characters in the Waverley Novels, are appropriately placed.

(b) *Grand Entrance to the Palace of Holyrood.* 1846.
Engraved by W. J. Linton. It measures 14.4 inches by 9.6.

(c) *View of Leith from the Martello Tower.* 1819.
An attractive picture of the Port, engraved by C. Thomson. As usual the Signal Tower is a prominent feature. A paddle-steamer leaving the harbour and the other shipping adds interest to the view.

In the 1947 volume of the Old Water Colour Society's publications there appears a reproduction of Roberts' picture *Edinburgh Castle from the Grassmarket,* 1822, a viewpoint which fascinated so many visiting artists to the City.

The great J. M. W. Turner was one of the outstanding artists who found in Edinburgh scenes worthy of his brush, and fully a dozen prints by William Miller (his favourite engraver), George Cooke, T. Higham, R. Wallis, and H.Le Keux are to be found in the Library collection. Those by Miller are mentioned on page 62.

Turner

Several of Turner's drawings were done for Scott's *Provincial Antiquities of Scotland*. The following may be briefly described :—

    (a) *High Street, Edinburgh,* engraved by H. Le Keux. 1819.
        A view down the great wide street, looking east. Eager sales-men are seen at their stalls, pedlars hawking their wares, and spectators strolling around enjoying the stir and bustle.

    (b) *Heriot's Hospital,* engraved by H. Le Keux. 1822.
        The Hospital is set high in the distance above the dwelling-houses below. The open space in the Grassmarket is filled with stalls and the scene is a busy and cheerful one.

    (c) *Edinburgh from Calton Hill,* engraved by G. Cooke. 1820.
        A bird's-eye view from the summit of the hill showing the great spread of the old town from the Castle along the City ridge. Women are spreading out clothes to dry or bleach, but the most interesting feature is the building of the Regent Bridge with the masons dressing the stones in the sheds adjacent to the new structure.

    (d) *Edinburgh from Firth of Forth,* engraved by R. Wallis. 1826.
        The view is really from Leith Harbour where a Man of War is saluting. A brilliant sun blazes down. At the bottom are two clasped hands between the stars of St. George and St. Andrew.

In the first two of these the figures were etched by G. Cooke.

    While in Edinburgh Turner frequently met Thomson of Duddingston, Hugh W. Williams (Grecian Williams) and other noted artists, and many were the discussions on art topics which took place at their meetings, particularly those at Duddingston Manse.

Turner de Lond   Mention of J. M. W. Turner reminds one of the prints of his contemporary of the same name, who signed his engravings W. Turner de Lond and created much confusion in the minds of collectors. He is best known by his drawings of the Great Fire of 1824 which destroyed so many of the buildings in Parliament Square. These were lithographed by Robertson and Ballantine, 20 Greenside Place. The devastating nature of the conflagration is well illustrated in the six prints noted below :—

    (a) *Great conflagration—Edinburgh as seen from the Calton Hill.*
        The dark silhouette of the Nelson Monument stands out

boldly to the left against the sky and is balanced by the Observatory on the right. A heavy pall of smoke fills the valley below and the lurid glare of the flames lights up the clouds overhead. This lithograph is coloured, an appropriate medium for such a subject.

(b) *Part of the ruins of the Great Fire from the High Street.*
St. Giles is the central feature. Spectators crowd the main thoroughfare, and an old-fashioned coach is seen in the foreground.

(c) *Conflagration of the Tron Church, Edinburgh, 16th November, 1824.*
The topmost portion of the church spire has already fallen and men are seen on the roof seeking to save the main part of the structure. The weathercock is toppling into the street and flames and smoke obscure much of the steeple. Cavalrymen keep back the great crowds. Far up the street the tower of St. Giles is seen rising above the billowing clouds of smoke.

(d) *View of the Great Fire in the Parliament Square, Edinburgh.*
St. Giles is seen to the left, giving an impression of a very fine and competent architectural drawing. Dragoons keep back the crowds of spectators. While firemen, policemen, and others carry on their duties amidst the smoke and flames, householders strive to salvage their precious furniture.

(e) *View of the Great Fire at Edinburgh, 1824.*
The whole line of the High Street is seen looking towards the Tron. Some of the towering blocks of buildings have already disappeared and the crumbling desolate ruins of others are bound to suffer the same tragic end. The rising smoke tells a tale of further damage.

(f) *Part of the ruins of the Great Fire, Edinburgh, as seen from the door of the Police Office.*
To the left a great gable appears to be on the point of falling. Injured people are being helped by police officers. The crown of St. Giles appears above the wreckage of burnt-out buildings.

In addition to these lithographs W. Turner de Lond did several drawings of which his coloured aquatint *Arrival of George IV at Palace of Holyrood* (described on page 88) ; *Broughton Street ; The Calton ;*

The Calton Hill, etc., Edinburgh from the North Bridge; and *Skating and Curling on Duddingston Loch near Edinburgh* are all most attractive items. *Broughton Street* and *The Calton* appeared in a series entitled *Scotia Delineata.* The former has as its most conspicuous feature the Roman Catholic Chapel, otherwise known as St. Mary's Cathedral. In a later issue of the series the print was simply titled Catholic Chapel.

Who was W. Turner de Lond ? There has been considerable dubiety on this point and for quite a number of collectors the unusual signature was just another example of the great J. M. W.'s eccentricity. Some aver that J. M. was known as W. Turner of London to distinguish him from W. Turner, the landscape artist of Oxford and a lengthy controversy raged in the *Connoiseur* of 1906 regarding the matter. A letter from Douglas A. Seton Steuart clinched the matter with his statement that " William Turner ' de Lond ' was employed by Sir Henry Steuart of Allanton, to illustrate a book which he published in 1827, and while at Allanton he gave drawing lessons to Sir Henry's daughter. He was probably a drawing master who came to settle in Edinburgh, or at any rate in Scotland, not later than 1822."

Many other artists—Ewbank, Somerville, Lizars, and Skene— were responsible for water colours, etchings, and lithographs illustrating the devastating effect of the great conflagration on the heavily built-up area in the very heart of the City.

Webster   About this period Mary Webster brought together in an album her water colour sketches of Scottish landscapes and the pages include twenty views of Edinburgh done between 1830-1840. Nothing is known of the artist who was obviously an amateur, but the sketches are quite pleasing and have value as illustrations of the first half of the 19th century.

Miller   No account of the engravers of Edinburgh could possibly omit the name of William Miller who was born in the City in 1801 and lived there for the most part of his long life. As a young man he was apprenticed to William Archibald, but later he went to London to study under George Cooke. According to Ruskin, Miller was the best engraver of Turner's works: at all events he was the best of the line engravers *after Turner.* Frederick Wedmore, in his book, *Fine Prints* says that " the work of William Miller interpreted with quite peculiar exquisiteness those refinements of light which in Turner's middle and later time so much engaged his effort."

The earliest engraving by Miller in the collection is *Lauriston Castle,* after a drawing by James Skene. The print, which dates from 1826, is a neat piece of work, full of promise for the young craftsman's future. Somewhat later come three of the Turner items—*Edinburgh from Blackford Hill, 1831; Edinburgh from St. Anthony's Chapel, 1836;* and *Craigmillar Castle, 1836.* In the St. Anthony's view the ruins of the ancient structure appear in deep shadow contrasting strongly with the City itself which is bathed in sunshine. The Castle is seen to the left and Calton Hill to the right, with Holyrood in the valley below.

Among his later work Miller did a fine engraving, *Edinburgh from Arthur's Seat,* after H. W. Williams. It was issued in 1845. The original water colour by Williams is in Huntly House.

Miller also engraved illustrations for Scott's works and vignette engravings for Hood's poems after Birket Foster. In the Miller Room in Lady Stair's House there are exhibited four steel plates made by Miller, a zincograph plate of Canongate Tolbooth, a copper plate of Coates House, a set of his engraving instruments, and other relics.

Miller died in 1882 and in 1886 a privately printed catalogue of his works was issued, along with a memoir of the engraver. The catalogue covers work done after such noted artists as D. O. Hill, E. L. Leitch, Clarkson Stanfield, and James Skene.

In 1834 a French artist, Joseph F. Dupressoir, did a sketch of Dupressoir *Edinburgh from Craig Leith Quarry* which was engraved by Kaeppelin. This painter, who lived from 1800-1859, has let his imagination run riot, for his drawing gives the impression of an Eastern scene with domes and minarets and towers. Even the three figures in the foreground are costumed like French peasants rather than staid Edinburgh citizens. The lithograph, which measures 12.3 inches by 9.2, is titled in both French and English.

Another foreigner's outlook on the Scottish Capital appeared in Hammer the following year—*Vue d'Edinbourg prise de Calton Hill,* a coloured aquatint by C. G. Hammer. The picture features the Calton Jail with the Governor's House and adjoining buildings, and a large timber yard to the east of the Jail. A line of trees fronts the prison. Looking towards the Castle and the Old Town one gets a slight glimpse of the Mound with the roof of the Rotunda showing just behind it. The print is an interesting one and well executed.

Moffat   About this period quite an unusual piece of engraved work origin-
ated in William Moffat's *Geometrical and Geological Landscape* with
tables of the relative altitudes of the ' principal public and other edifices,
squares and hills situate in the City of Edinburgh and the Environs.'
Moffat was a land surveyor of Knightsbridge, London, and the engraving was done by W. H. Lizars in 1837. There are no fewer than 300
small pictures within the plate, each carefully numbered and lined up
in order of the index key. Arthur's Seat, Salisbury Crags, the inn at
Hunter's Tryst, St. Giles, the University and other places are included
in the orderly array. The measurements in feet and inches are taken
from the high water mark of the sea at the tide gauge at the lock gates
of the West Dock, Leith. The *Landscape* was published by A. and C.
Black of Edinburgh and London.

Swarbreck   In 1837 Samuel D. Swarbreck issued a folio series of lithographs
which are frequently met with in separate form. The volume was
entitled *Sketches in Scotland, drawn from nature and on stone.* The
plates are large sized, measuring approximately 16 x 12 inches each,
and fifteen of them represent views in Edinburgh. They have one
characteristic feature. Where figures are introduced into the scene the
artist has frequently contrived to include at least one Highlander, dear
old ladies in poke bonnets escorted by courtly gentlemen in ' toppers '
and frock coats with broad check trousers, and sometimes Newhaven
fishwives in their voluminous garb. The effect is pleasing enough but
tends to become rather monotonous from frequent repetition.

The view, *Royal Institution, Castle, and Princes Street,* illustrated
here is a typical example of his work. Another representative specimen
is entitled *Edinburgh Castle from the Grassmarket* and to balance it
there is the print *Edinburgh from the Calton Hill.* They make a fine
pair—well worthy of a place in the collection.

The remaining lithographs include five of Holyrood and Queen
Mary's apartments, High Street, High School Wynd, the University,
Regent's Bridge, Edinburgh from above Dugald Stewart's Monument,
and the North Bridge.

A coloured set of these lithographs was issued but it is very scarce.

Kemp   The name of George Meikle Kemp will always be associated with
the Scott Monument. A self taught artist, he used his natural talent
to preserve for us some attractive views of the City.

Among these the most important is Brown and Somerville's

PLATE 38

TRINITY COLLEGE CHURCH, LOW CALTON
Coloured lithograph by R. Carrick after W. L. Leitch. c. 1850

PLATE 39

BAILIE FYFE'S CLOSE
Water colour by J. Drummond. 1845

John Knox's House—1854

PLATE 40

JOHN KNOX'S HOUSE
Lithograph from a pencil sketch by J. Drummond. 1854

*G

PLATE 41

The Royal Institution, Edinburgh
Lithograph by S. D. Swarbeck. 1837

aquatint of the Scott Monument, a large sized item measuring 14.1 inches by 19.5. This sketch covers the main features of the great structure in Princes Street with its four arched base supporting the central tower. It is dedicated to William Cowan, Esquire, a subscriber to the Auxiliary Fund. The print is a most effective one showing how finely the Monument stands out against the background of the old town.

In 1843 Kemp drew three sketches of the Calton Hill, all of them concerned with the National Monument and proposals for completing it. Nichol, J. West, and T. Dick were the respective engravers. The largest is that engraved by Nichol. It illustrates Kemp's strong leanings towards classical effects. The great National Monument is shown completed. On a lower level is the Royal High School, and also in the picture are the memorials to Burns and Dugald Stewart. This quartette of examples of Grecian architecture is in severely classical tradition and the likeness to the great structures on the Acropolis is indeed striking. West's engraving is really a smaller version of that of Nichol with some slight changes in the figures shown in the larger print. The third view by Dick is also on a small scale and shows the sad appearance of the uncompleted structure on the hilltop.

Another of Kemp's drawings, *View in Edinburgh from St. Anton's Well,* again shows the completed Monument with the inclusion below of Regent Terrace. It is a pleasing engraving in colour, done in 1843 and measuring 7 inches by 3.8. These sketches are clear evidence of Kemp's interest in the great National project, and though neither his nor any other drawings produced any effect they were important as pioneer efforts to achieve something permanent to replace the solitary pillars on the hilltop.

A sketch, *St. Giles Church, Edinburgh,* engraved by T. Dick is a typical City street scene with the great church in the background. Crowds of people throng the pavements, some with sunshades and others gossiping at the street well. Fishwives, stall holders proffering their wares, horsemen, and others form a happy grouping. On the back of the print we are informed

> " It is rarely that so much justice is done to the appropriate subject. With the aid of a glass every almost stone can be distinguished separately from the others."

The last item in the collection, *The Royal Institution,* engraved by W. Deeble, is yet another excellent example of Kemp's work. The Castle is partly seen in the background.

As is well known Kemp was accidentally drowned in the Canal Basin on a foggy night only a few months before the great memorial to Scott was completed. By his early death Edinburgh lost one of its most distinguished citizens.

Nichol   An engraver of marked ability was Nichol whose coloured lithograph *St. John's Chapel, Princes Street, from Castle Terrace* after W. Mason is illustrated here. This view appears to have been done about 1845. The south front of the chapel is the focal point of the picture with the glorious dome of St. George's Church seen on the left above the roof tops of the houses at the extreme end of Princes Street. On the right the sturdy spire of St. Cuthbert's gives balance to the scene. The broad sweep of King's Stables Road and the figures on pavement and street combine to form a most effective composition.

Another coloured lithograph after W. Mason is the *Canongate Tolbooth,* executed about 1840. This print, of much poorer quality than the above, shows a crowded street.

Three other of Nichol's coloured lithographs are worthy of mention—*Edinburgh from the north;* and *Princes Street, Edinburgh, looking West; with proposed Scott Monument, c. 1840,* both after J. Gordon, Jr., and *Head of the West Bow, High Street, Edinburgh.* This was also done about 1840.

Hardiviller   About 1836 a French artist, D'Hardiviller, who lived in Edinburgh for a time, drew and engraved a view of the Assembly Rooms in George Street under the title *Bal Celtique.* This coloured lithograph measuring 19.3 inches by 15, illustrates a great social event in January, 1836. The ball was given to provide financial aid and encouragement for the Highland schools under the patronage of the Highland Society. Among those present were the Duke and Duchess of Buccleuch, the Earl of Aboyne, the Marquis of Douglas, Lord Jeffrey, Sir T. Dick Lauder, and indeed most of the notable personages of the time. The proceedings started at 9 o'clock in the evening and carriages were engaged to call for the weary but happy guests at 6 a.m. next morning.

To create the right atmosphere for this great function the vestibule of the Assembly Rooms was fitted up as an ancient baronial hall and hung with tartans and appropriate Highland effects. A lengthy and detailed account of this great *Bal* is given in *The Scotsman* of January 30, 1836. The print is an interesting one with an appeal for those studying social history as well as for the print collector.

Recently the Library acquired a volume of original drawings by Grant James Grant entitled *A Collection of Sketches, Plans, Details, etc. From old buildings, particularly in and around Edinburgh, drawn by me, chiefly between 1840 & 1850.*

This collection of drawings is a valuable contribution to the Edinburgh scene. Grant was novelist, historian, draughtsman, and artist, and he exercised his talent in the illustration of his works. The drawings were done while he was in residence at 26 Danube Street, Stockbridge.

The volume contains over 400 sketches—pen and pencil drawings, water colours, architectural plans, details of notable features of old buildings, sketches of monuments of antiquarian interest, and similar material. All the items are signed and many of them are dated. About half of them are concerned with Edinburgh subjects, and frequently manuscript notes are given to supplement or explain the sketches.

Trinity College Church receives particular attention with 24 pages devoted to it. A fine plan of the building, with outstanding features numbered and identified by a manuscript list, was drawn from measurement on 6th November, 1847. Next come two full page sketches of the church, one in colour and one in sepia, taken from different viewpoints; a sketch of the sacristy and its doorway; a plan and doorway of the south porch; and finely executed drawings of the capitals, gargoyles, canopies, and brackets and buttresses, columns, and other features. These sketches form as complete a record as any to be found elsewhere. They are of special interest in view of the part Grant played in the controversy which raged round the proposals for the demolition of this famous ecclesiastical foundation.

Craigmillar Castle is covered in almost as full detail as Trinity College Kirk. Most of the sketches are related to projects for the restoration of the building. The first was based on old drawings and Grant's own observation. It is in colour. Other elevations of the proposed restoration are given from the north-west, north, west, and east. The chapel, rather like St. Margaret's Chapel in Edinburgh Castle, is illustrated by plan, sketch, details of windows, etc., and there are further pen drawings of coats of arms, sculptured stones, dovecot, and gates. To supplement these there is an attractive water colour of the castle drawn by Grant's mother, Mary Anne Watson, from whom he must have inherited some of his artistic talents.

Other items of note in the volume are the pages devoted to the sculptured stones of Edinburgh, all sketched with meticulous care. Many of the illustrations are of old buildings now swept away such as Hamilton's Folly in the Pleasance, Hardwell Close in Leith, Valleyfield House, Broadstair's House and the Dean House.

It would be impossible to give here a complete list of the varied selection of sketches, but what has been said above may give an idea of Grant's important contribution to the topographical field. In characteristic style his last sketch is a front elevation of a *Design for a Cathedral* by himself. If it had ever been built it would have been a fitting tribute to one who did so much for literature and for the history of his native City.

As has already been indicated the demolition of Trinity College Church was not accomplished without considerable opposition, and two suggestions at least were put forward for saving the venerable structure. D. Bryce's print, *Trinity College Church, as restored on the Calton Hill* was drawn by L. Ghemar and engraved by Schenck and McFarlane in 1852. The lithograph measures 17.1 inches by 12. The architect's solution of an awkward problem, however, found no favour with the authorities and nothing was done about it. The second solution was outlined in *The Scotsman* of May 6th, 1854. In brief, the proposal was to re-erect the old building in the Castle as a garrison chapel on the site occupied by the northern portion of the Armoury. The promoters of the scheme were of opinion that the site would be a most imposing one and that the church as viewed from Princes Street and other points would present a magnificent spectacle. As far as the writer knows there is no illustrated material relating to this project.

Wilson   Sir Daniel Wilson was a contemporary of Grant. He was apprenticed to William Miller. Later he went to London for further experience, but returned to Edinburgh in 1842 and set up business as a print-seller and artist's colourman in West Register Street. This brought him into contact with many eminent citizens, and his appointment as Secretary of the Society of Antiquaries of Scotland gave him still further opportunities for meeting people engaged in historical and archaeological research.

Wilson's most important work, *Memorials of Edinburgh in the Olden Time,* was issued in 24 parts in 1847, and in complete form in two volumes in 1848. They contain over 120 engraved illustrations—" pen-and-pencil sketches, professing in general considerable minuteness of outline, though with a rapid touch that precluded very elaborate finish. Accuracy has been aimed at throughout, not without knowingly incurring the risk of occasionally being somewhat dry." Dry some of his notes may have been but for him " the old legends and traditions of Edinburgh's closes and wynds, and the historical memories that haunted them " were all in all.

Wilson's drawings were engraved by William Forrest who lived for many years at 17 Archibald Place. Forrest also worked for Horatio McCulloch, Sam Bough, and others. Several of his engravings, with Sir Daniel's explicit instructions for improving them, are in the Library collection, and there is also one with the appreciative signed note by Sam Bough—" Capital, couldn't be better."

The names of Clarkson Stanfield, W. L. Leitch, and J. D. Harding ought to be considered together for they collaborated extensively round about 1850.

Stanfield was a well known marine painter who made two fine Stanfield drawings from sketches by Leitch. The first is a lithograph *The Back of the old Leith Pier,* a structure which was erected during the early part of the 17th century and withstood the stormy seas for over 200 years. On the left is seen the Signal Tower, a prominent feature of all seaward views of Leith. It was originally a windmill and was constructed by Robert Mylne in 1685 who also built the sea wall at Leith, erected many important buildings in the principal streets of Edinburgh, and built Mylne's Mount, one of the bastions of Edinburgh Castle. The second was *Barnbougle Castle,* a lovely coloured lithograph giving a view of the Firth and its shipping and small boats on the shore. Both of these prints were engraved by Harding. Another of their combined efforts was *Edinburgh from the Firth of Forth,* a very attractive coloured lithograph. Though undated these three prints can safely be assigned to 1854.

Stanfield did two other drawings entitled *Firth of Forth* and *View of Edinburgh from the Village of Dean,* which he had engraved by E. Finden. The first, like the sea scenes noted above, illustrates his flair for setting down his impressions of everything connected with the sea. For this he has sometimes been called the English Vandevelde after the famous Dutch painter.

The second is a view from the North West " looking up the Kirk-brae towards Edinburgh from a short distance up the old Queensferry or Belford Road." The Library has no copy of this print, but it is illustrated in volume 25 of *The Book of the Old Edinburgh Club* in an article by John Clark Wilson dealing with the lands and houses of Drumsheugh.

Ruskin said of Stanfield that he was " incomparably the noblest master of cloud form of all our artists."

Leitch   William Leighton Leitch was a landscape painter who lived from 1804 to 1883 and did his best work about the middle of the century. He had a Scottish connection as he was at one time employed as a scene painter at the Glasgow Theatre and also as an actor. Large separate plates have been executed from his drawings. Twelve of his sketches are reproduced in the print collection, eight of them engraved by J. D. Harding. These lithographs are among the finest in the collection and include Barnbougle Castle, Edinburgh Castle from the Grassmarket, Edinburgh from Craigleith Quarry, Edinburgh from the Firth of Forth, Edinburgh from the Mound, Head of the West Bow, New Assembly Hall, St. Bernard's Well.

Leitch's drawings are characterised by his colourful composition and real feeling for atmosphere. The Harding lithographs bring out most faithfully these aspects of Leitch's drawings.

Stanfield, Leitch, and David Roberts contributed drawings for Lawson's *Scotland Delineated,* a folio in two volumes issued between 1847-54. They were also associated with William Miller, who executed plates for Stanfield's *Holyrood from the Calton-Hill* and *View from James' Court,* both good examples of Miller's work.

Harding   J. D. Harding, lithographer and painter, lived from 1798 to 1863 and was thus a contemporary of Stanfield and Leitch. He came to Edinburgh as a young lad and was apprenticed to a heraldic painter. He became acquainted with David Roberts who was at that time employed in the Theatre Royal, and no doubt the friendship engendered between the two was beneficial to the younger man. Among his earlier works were 50 plates done in 1836 entitled *Sketches at Home and Abroad.* Five years later he had published *The Park and the Forest* in which he experimented with sketching direct on the stone with a brush instead of a crayon, a method to which he gave the name lithotint. His last work of importance and his finest achievement was his *Picturesque Selections* done in 1861. He was particularly versatile in depicting trees and architectural studies. He is represented in the collection by 20 lithographs of quality including the Stanfield items already noted. These are after noted artists such as his friend David Roberts, W. L. Leitch, and G. Cattermole. Particularly fine are the two drawings of Roberts of *Craigmillar Castle* and *Edinburgh from the Castle,* the first of which gives him scope for his skilful treatment of trees. His *National Monument, Calton Hill* was another attempt to stimulate afresh an interest in one of Edinburgh's unfinished projects.

A writer in the *Art Journal* of 1850 says of Harding that " into whatever remote corner of the world the art of lithography has penetrated the sketches of this accomplished draughtsman have found their way." And speaking of other aspects of his work he mentions particularly his cloud effects and quotes

" Those two are Harding's cloud, so heapeth he
Their pillowy beauty (so the giants heaped
Ossa on Pelion) ; some have edges steeped
In sunlight. Some float dark and solemnly,
Some slope their dusky shadows of thick rain."

Harding's two lithographs after W. L. Leitch—*Head of the West Bow* and *St. Bernard's Well*—were both executed in 1854, and are equally fascinating. The West Bow scene is typical of the period, with its pleasing groups of residents in the neighbourhood. The view of St. Bernard's Well emphasises the severely classical design of Alexander Nasmyth. Behind the Grecian temple is St. George's Well, to the left the lade for Canonmills, and above it the houses on Randolph Cliff. In the background is the Dean Bridge and among the trees on the right appears the Church of the Holy Trinity. It is interesting to compare this print with the water colour of the same scene by J. C. Ibbetson which is also in the collection.

Harding's friendship with George Cattermole, the well-known Cattermole English painter and illustrator, resulted in some fine lithographs of Edinburgh scenes after sketches by that noted artist. These included the following prints, all dated about 1854 :—

Dowie's Tavern, Libberton's Wynd.
Fleshmarket Close, Edinburgh.
West Bow.
Foot of the West Bow.

Old Greyfriars Churchyard, signing the National Covenant.
Queen Mary's Bed-chamber, Holyrood House.
A wash drawing of the West Bow is also in the collection.

Cattermole found in the *Waverley Novels* an attractive subject for his brush, and 21 engravings from his original drawings appeared in Leitch Ritchie's *Scott and Scotland,* published by Longman in 1835. Four Edinburgh items were included in the work—smaller versions of the large lithographs listed above, which were his contribution to J. P. Lawson's *Scotland Delineated* for which many noted artists submitted their sketches. Ritchie's work was translated into French—*Walter Scott et les Ecossais*—and the same illustrations were used in the Continental text.

Though Cattermole began his career as an architectural draughtsman, he had a fine sense of colour and a marked feeling for the romantic spirit of earlier days. This is illustrated by the notes appended to the lithographs. In *The West Bow,* for example, we are informed that dagger makers were the principal residents, and when that trade became extinct they were succeeded by white iron smiths, white smiths, copper smiths, and pewterers. The armed men in the crowded street are certainly well equipped with swords and daggers and are apparently prepared to make good use of them!

Channing   The sketches of William Channing date from the middle of the 19th century. He is represented by eight pencil and wash drawings, mostly of the closes of the Royal Mile, and a striking collection of sketches in three volumes which formed part of the Cowan Bequest. These provide topographical details of old and famous City buildings not readily available elsewhere, and on more than one occasion they have proved of value to those seeking material relating to the architectural features of the closes and wynds which are gradually being replaced by more modern structures.

Little is known of Channing, but in Gilpin's *Sam Bough, R.S.A.* it is stated that at one time he was a scene painter at the Theatre Royal, Manchester. Later he came to Scotland and in Edinburgh he was apparently employed in a similar capacity in the Theatre Royal for his name appears frequently in the playbills issued from that theatre. In his declining years Sam Bough, who had been one of his pupils, cared for him until his death in Leith.

PLATE 42

THE BACK OF THE OLD LEITH PIER
Lithograph by J. D. Harding after C. Stanfield. c. 1854

J.D.H.

W. L. Leitch

PLATE 43

EDINBURGH CASTLE FROM THE GRASSMARKET

Lithograph by J. D. Harding after W. L. Leitch. c. 1854

PLATE 44

EDINBURGH FROM THE MOUND
Lithograph by J. D. Harding after W. L. Leitch. c. 1854

PLATE 45

NEW ASSEMBLY HALL
Lithograph by J. D. Harding after W. L. Leitch. c. 1854

The eight pencil and wash drawings referred to above are :—

Advocates Close. 1849.
At the back of the clothes shop, High Street. 1849.
Cottages at Broughton, near E. Claremont Street. c. 1850.
High School Wynd, east side. c. 1850.
Kinniburgh's Close, Grassmarket. c. 1850.
Old Playhouse Close. 1849.
Reid's Close, Canongate. c. 1850.
West Port. c. 1850.

The three volumes contain 147 sketches in pencil and wash, none of which have been reproduced. As some indication of the contents one might mention four drawings of Riddle's Court, a notable building in the Lawnmarket, dating from 1726. The ancient structure still exists and it is of interest to remember that David Hume, the great philosopher went to live there in 1751. Later still the family of James Skene of Rubislaw, Sir Walter Scott's greatest friend, made their home there. In his manuscript volume, *Reekiana,* Skene describes in vivid style that eventful evening in 1783 when the ' flitting ' reached the City. It was the King's Birthday and the three roomy carriages with the members of the family inside had to run the gauntlet of the great crowds celebrating the day with bonfires and fireworks. Over the North Bridge the frightened horses raced past the revellers, and it was with great relief that the family ultimately arrived safely at the inn in Mylne's Court where they were to spend the night, before proceeding next day to Shawfield's Lodging in Riddle's Court. Like David Roberts in later years the young Skene found adjacent cellar doors most useful as canvasses for setting down in chalk his first sketches. These early efforts bore much fruit as the chapter on the Skene drawings will show. The four sketches are illustrative of the remaining contents of the volumes. In a lecture on the Cowan Collection Dr. Savage said of them

" Topographically they were excellent because the artist was careful in drawing the details which enabled the topographers to identify the buildings."

At the sale of Sam Bough's effects in 1879 a volume of sketches of military and other costumes from the 10th century, drawn and coloured by Channing, was sold for five guineas.

Drummond   An important figure in Edinburgh art circles during the early part of the 19th century was James Drummond who secured a reputation for depicting most colourfully scenes of historic and antiquarian interest. He was born in 1816 in John Knox's House and one can well believe that his future fondness for the olden times can be traced to his early environment. For our purpose his great merit lies in the fine collection of pencil and wash drawings of the closes, wynds, streets and buildings done between the years 1848 and 1859 and later incorporated in the lithographic reproductions of the folio volume entitled *Old Edinburgh*. These lithographs are of fine quality and have a high topographic value as material for the student and research worker.

One of the most attractive of these lithographs is *John Knox's House,* a view which incorporates also Moubray House and the street well for the residents in this quaint corner of the High Street. The house was erected about 1550. The original entrance was by a door, now built up, in the north-west angle. The outside stair is a comparatively modern addition. The roof was covered in grey stones, the present red tiles being a recent feature. The first owners were John Mosman, goldsmith to Mary Queen of Scots, and his wife Marion Aires. Their initials and arms are on the outside wall.

Drummond is also represented in the collection by a fine water colour of Bailie Fyfe's Close, a typical example of the closes which are still common in the Old Town. The overhanging storey above the outside stair was characteristic of many of these tenement dwellings, but most of them have now disappeared. Another delightful water colour— *College Wynd, 1852*—hangs in Huntly House.

Drummond did a sketch of the interior of St. Giles for the original edition of Sir Daniel Wilson's *Memorials of Edinburgh in the Olden Time.* His membership of the Society of Antiquaries, for which he contributed many articles to the *Proceedings,* no doubt brought him much into contact with Sir Daniel.

In 1868 Drummond became Curator of the National Gallery, a position which he held until his death in 1877.

Le Conte   Somewhat later than Drummond we have the work of John Le Conte who lived from 1816-1877. Some thirty of his water colours are in the Edinburgh Room or hung in Huntly House. Among them are two striking pictures of the old Theatre Royal in Shakespeare Square, a view of Jenny Ha's Change House illustrating a typical tavern of his own times, three sketches of Cardinal Beaton's House in the Cowgate, three of the Watergate, and other places which have long since disappeared. His engravings of Wilkie's *Parliament Close* and James Edgar's picture *Dr. Guthrie among the street urchins at the West Bow* indicate his keen interest in street scenes and City characters. Le Conte must have been a prolific worker for many of his sketches can still be picked up in the premises of art dealers in the City.

One of the most energetic and skilful artists of the mid-nineteenth century was Robert W. Billings who lived from 1813-1874. His greatest achievement was *The Baronial and Ecclesiastical Antiquities* of Scotland issued between the years 1845 and 1852. It contained 240 illustrations of notable buildings, an architectural and artistic record which has probably never been equalled. Billings was undoubtedly one of the greatest architectural draughtsmen which this country has produced. Many of the drawings were engraved by John Le Keux, including those of Craigmillar Castle, Heriot's Hospital, St. Giles' Cathedral, and Trinity College Church executed between 1845 and 1847. Le Keux did his first experimental engraving on pewter and when he found the touch for working on that metal he proceeded to engrave on both copper and steel. The steel engravings for Billing's monumental work are among the finest examples done in that medium. According to Redgrave Le Keux became the " best engraver of his day in the somewhat mechanical style then in vogue." In this instance the somewhat disparaging criticism would appear a trifle harsh as the delineation of buildings hardly lends itself to the free treatment of a landscape or other subject where the imagination and skilled technique of the artist gets full play.

Billings' association with Edinburgh was strengthened when he was commissioned to supervise the restoration of the chapel of Edinburgh Castle.

John Le Keux's brother Henry also favoured Edinburgh subjects for in 1826 he engraved in fine style A. W. Callcott's drawing *The Castle from the Grassmarket*, J. M. W. Turner's *Heriot's Hospital from the foot of the West Bow, 1822,* and the same artist's *High Street, Edinburgh, 1819.* In these three plates the figures were etched by G. Cooke—a characteristic example of engravers working together to secure the best results.

75

6

MISCELLANEOUS AND LATER PRINTS

AMONG the miscellaneous prints and drawings which do not fit in well to the chronological sequence on which the main body of the text is arranged the following merit attention. Unless otherwise stated the artists or engravers are unknown.

(a) The Canongate Tolbooth. 1829.

A view taken from the west. The building was erected in 1591 and occupies the site of a previous one commonly designated the ' Auld Tolbuith.' After the erection of the Calton Jail this edifice was used for the imprisonment of debtor's only. The Canongate remained a separate Burgh of Regality until absorbed by the municipality of Edinburgh in 1856. Of recent years the building has been used by the Corporation for various purposes, and only a few months ago it was opened, after reconstruction, as an addition to the local museums controlled by the Libraries Committee on their behalf. The restoration has been carried out in most careful fashion to show the style of the former stonework, panelling, and plasterwork, and one of the cells formerly used for the incarceration of criminals has been preserved in the basement of the building. This pen and wash drawing measures 18.5 inches by 11.8.

(b) Portobello near Edinburgh. c. 1834.

A faint pencil sketch against the background of Arthur's Seat. The view appears to be from the Joppa end, showing the road from Musselburgh.

(c) Village of Portobello about 1850

The seaside suburb prior to the erection of the pier. In the foreground are holiday-makers and a number of old-fashioned horse drawn bathing coaches. On the extreme right is the old Portobello Tower, built in 1785 and later allowed to fall into a ruinous state. Hugh Paton, the publisher of Kay's *Portraits,* restored it as a dwelling-house about 1864. In the background may be seen the spire of the church in Melville Street. The drawing is in pencil and wash, and measures 11.5 inches by 7.3.

(d) Edinburgh from Ravelston, by Horatio McCulloch. 1841.
An oil painting exhibited in Huntly House. A fine example of this artist's work, showing Arthur's Seat in the background to the right, Berwick Law in the distance to the left, and the stretch of country-side between the suburb and the City proper.

(e) Edinburgh looking South East. c. 1840.
A panoramic effect in oils with the North Bridge and the Old Town as the outstanding features. It measures approximately 5 feet by 18 inches and hangs in Huntly House.

(f) High School Yards, by John Glass. c. 1850.
The interest of this oil painting lies in the overhanging storeys of the old building, very similar to those of the Bowhead House, with strong pillars to carry the overhead weight. Hung in Huntly House.

(g) Mercat Cross, by Lauder Sawers. 1885.
A large water colour illustrating the presentation of the restored market cross to the Magistrates and Council by the Rt. Hon. W. E. Gladstone. Measuring approximately 4 feet by 3 this fine piece of work is a record of a great occasion in the history of the City. In Huntly House.

(h) North British Railway from the North Bridge, by T. Steuart. 1846.
This neat little print shows the trains puffing past Trinity College Church and the sheds where passengers boarded the very primitive early trains. An admiring crowd of spectators are as much interested in the ' Puffing Billies ' of those days as present day children who love to watch the trains go by.

(i) The Low Calton, by J. Rose, 1848.
A photograph from a picture of an oil painting in the possession of Mr. Richard J. Simpson of Corstorphine. It gives another impression, from a slightly different viewpoint of the scene described in the Steuart print noted above.

So far I have dealt only with prints and drawings from the earliest times to about 1850. Some few items of slightly later date have actually been included as certain artists and engravers have done work both before and after that year. To list and describe the work of recent contributors to the Edinburgh scene would be a formidable task but it may be well to give a brief outline of some of the more important recent sets which are to be found in the Edinburgh Room, without in any way attempting to describe the separate items in detail.

Aikman   In Huntly House there are over twenty water colours by George Aikman who flourished from 1860-1905. These original sketches deal mainly with old closes and buildings in and around the Royal Mile. They are uniform in size, about 7 inches by 10, and are excellent examples of topographical drawing.

Diaz   Robert Diaz is represented by some 20 items, some in the Edinburgh Room and some in Huntly House. They include both pencil drawings and water colours similar in scope to those of Aikman. Most of them were done between 1880 and 1890.

Ross   Next there are 53 drawings by Dr. Thomas Ross, joint author with David MacGibbon of that notable work *The Castellated and Domestic Architecture of Scotland* and other architectural works. These drawings combine artistic skill with the accuracy of the experienced architect. They date from 1870-1920 or thereby and represent a considerable body of work to which reference is frequently made by students of Scottish traditional architecture.

Home   Contemporary with Dr. Ross a most capable local artist, Bruce J. Home, produced a series of lithographs, pencil drawings, and etchings which together form a striking record of the past glories of the City. His *Old Houses in Edinburgh,* published in two volumes from 1905-1907, is his outstanding contribution to the artistic interpretation of local topography. In a preface to the work the artist assures us that, of the 40 sketches included, all were drawn on the spot with the exception of John Knox's House and the Canongate Tolbooth. So far as the first of these was concerned he thought it advisable to show the relationship of the house to the old Netherbow Port which was demolished in 1764. His sketch is based very largely on the well known Runciman drawing mention of which is made on page 17, and a very pleasing piece of reconstruction it is. The Tolbooth sketch shows the old projecting clock supported on oaken beams before it was superseded by the present timepiece.

Smith   Another set of fine water colours of scenes in Edinburgh and its neighbourhood was the work of Mrs. Jane Stewart Smith, the author of *The Grange of St. Giles,* 1898, and *Historic Stones and Stories of Bygone*

Edinburgh, 1924. She spared no pains to secure accurate details of her selected subjects and was fortunate enough to get certain of the drawings done while the buildings were in process of demolition. According to her own account, she frequently set out to sketch between the hours of 4-6 a.m. on summer mornings " to catch the reverberating echoes of the past as they linger round the old historic buildings." Most of her sketches are reproduced in the two works noted above, but lacking the colour, the illustrations do not have the pleasing effect of the original water colours now exhibited in Huntly House in the Canongate where much of the artist's work was done. The sketches include many unusual subjects not illustrated elsewhere—Old Hallow Fair, Grassmarket; Cant's Close; Corridor in Lord Haliburton's House; Porteous Mob Corner. A particularly fine sketch of Holyrood Chapel recently acquired is probably her best contribution.

Still another set of 51 water colours by James Steuart is included in the collection. The artist was the author of *Sketching in Water Colours,* and *Sketching Ways and Sketching Days,* two books much used by amateur artists.

Steuart

We have now passed into the photographic age in which the camera and the film take a foremost place in visual education and recreation, along with the new offset and other processes which have been so greatly developed by the printing houses of the country, and are so widely used for illustration in books and periodicals nowadays. At its best this new style has much to commend it, but the keen collector will still find in the early views and engravings a most fascinating field in which to work.

7

PANORAMIC VIEWS

Barker   BY virtue of picturesque setting and the numerous viewpoints within the City area it is not surprising that the artist's eye readily took note of these aesthetic advantages. They made a particularly strong appeal to the panoramic artists, of whom Robert Barker was the pioneer and also the most enterprising of those who sought to set on canvas or paper their impressions of the burgh and its notable buildings. Unlike Gordon's bird's-eye view of 1647, in which only the compact and generally overcrowded mass of structures within the Flodden Wall was depicted, the panoramic artists set themselves to cover an extensive terrain in detail. Many of their sketches were quite remarkable.

Barker is said to have invented this type of topographic view which was executed " on the system of curvilinear perspective applied to a concave subject so as to appear level from a certain station-point." Working to this plan he drew his panoramic view in six great sections and had them engraved in aquatinta by J. Wells. Each of the sections measures 21.7 inches by 16.7 and, when mounted together, they occupy a wall space of approximately 11 feet. These sections illustrate very clearly the lay-out of the City in the year 1793 as seen in different directions from the Calton Hill. A key issued with them enables one to identify the outstanding buildings. This key is an unusual production, apparently issued from Leicester Square, where Barker sought a wider field for this and the other panoramic views which he had drawn. It is in diagrammatic form. In the centre circle there appears the following advertisement :—

> " Now exhibiting in the second circle, a view of Edinburgh and surrounding country. The Contemplation of this grand and delightful Scene and an earnest Desire to represent it entire, were the first Circumstances which impressed Mr. Barker's Mind with the idea of a Panorama. The Public may now form a judgment

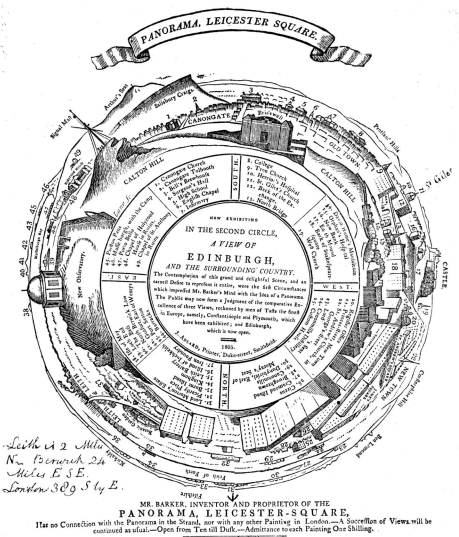

NOW EXHIBITING

IN THE SECOND CIRCLE,

A VIEW OF

EDINBURGH,

AND THE SURROUNDING COUNTRY.

The Contemplation of this grand and delightful Scene, and an earneſt Deſire to repreſent it entire, were the firſt Circumſtances which impreſſed Mr. Barker's Mind with the Idea of a Panorama. The Public may now form a Judgment of the comparative Ex- cellence of three Views, reckoned by men of Taſte the fineſt in Europe, namely, Conſtantinople and Plymouth, which have been exhibited ; and Edinburgh, which is now open.

1805.

J. ADLARD, Printer, Duke-street, Smithfield.

1. Canongate Church
2. Canongate Tolbooth
3. Bell's Brewhouſe
4. Surgeon's Hall
5. High School
6. Engliſh Chapel
7. Infirmary

8. College
9. Tron Church
10. Herriot's Hoſpital
11. St. Giles's Church
12. Back of the Ex-change.
13. North Bridge

SOUTH.

WEST.

EAST.

NORTH.

Leith is 2 Miles
N. Berwick 24
Miles E. S E.
London 389 S by E.

PLATE 46

KEY TO BARKER'S PANORAMA
Engraving. 1793

PLATE 47

THE CANONGATE TOLBOOTH, 1829
Pen and wash drawing, artist unknown

PLATE 48

OLD BOWHEAD AND LAWNMARKET

Coloured lithograph by J. D. Harding after W. L. Leitch. c. 1854

H

PLATE 49

ST. BERNARD'S WELL, WATER OF LEITH, EDINBURGH
Coloured lithograph by J. D. Harding after W. L. Leitch. c. 1854

PLATE 50

NATIONAL MONUMENT, CALTON HILL
Coloured lithograph by J. D. Harding. c. 1854

PLATE 51

New College Quadrangle
Water colour by T. Ross. 1869

PLATE 52

VILLAGE OF PORTOBELLO
Pencil and wash drawing, artist unknown. c. 1850

I

PLATE 53   DOWIE'S TAVERN, LIBBERTON'S WYND
Lithograph by J. D. Harding after G. Cattermole

of the comparative Excellence of three Views, reckoned by men of Taste the finest in Europe, namely Constantinople and Plymouth, which have been exhibited ; and Edinburgh, which is now open."

Beyond this central circle with its flattering description of the City, there is a list of 49 items of interest in the sketches, supplemented by neat little drawings on the outer fringes of the bill. Evidently Barker had a business-like as well as an artistic approach to his work !

Barker's great panoramic sweep begins at the foot of the Canongate where it takes in the Canongate Church and Tolbooth, Bell's Brewhouse, Surgeon's Hall, the High School, the English Chapel, and the Infirmary. Thereafter it continues it circular progress round the City until the sixth and last part of the tour shows the new Observatory, with numerous astronomical instruments set up on the lawns, and Portobello, Mussel- burgh, and the background of Arthur's Seat and the Crags.

The 49 points of interest listed in Barker's eulogistic key to his great panorama are as follows :—

1. Canongate Church
2. Canongate Tolbooth
3. Bell's Brewhouse
4. Surgeon's Hall
5. High School
6. English Chapel
7. Infirmary
8. College
9. Tron Church
10. Herriot's Hospital
11. St. Giles's Church
12. Back of the Exchange
13. North Bridge
14. David Hume's Mausoleum
15. Orphan's Hospital
16. New Bank
17. Earth Mound
18. Back of Shakespeare Square
19. West Church
20. Register Office

21. Princes Street, New Town
22. St. Andrew's Church, in George Street
23. Lord Rosebery's Seat
24. Canonmills Distillery
25. Custom House
26. Circus
27. Cramond Island
28. Broughtown
29. Canonmills
30 Dunybirsel (Donibristle) Earl of Moray's Seat
31. Lord Morton's Estate
32. Picardy Place
33. Burnt Island
34. Kinghorn
35. Leith Battery
36. Island of Inchkeith
37. Iron Foundry
38. Isle of May

39. Loch End
40. The Bass
41. North Berwick Law
42. Gosfort, Earl of Wemys
43. Port Seaton
44. Barracks
45. Preston Pans

46. Musselburgh, with the Camp
47. Porto Bello
48. Chapel of Holyrood House in ruins
49. Chapel of St. Anthony in ruins

Lady Elton

In 1820 Mary Stewart, afterwards Lady Elton, drew a set of views entitled *Four Panoramic Views of Edinburgh and the surrounding Country from the top of Blackford Hill.* They were engraved by C. Hullmandel, an artist whose treatment gives an almost pastel effect. These lithographic sheets are much more rural in aspect than the Barker aquatints and cover a stretch of country far beyond the limits of his panorama. Roughly speaking their range is as follows :—

1. Kames Hill and Dalmahoy Crags to Corstorphine.
2. Corstorphine to Arthur's Seat. Though again a somewhat rural scene it shows such places as St. George's Church, St. John's Chapel, West Church, the Castle, Heriot's, St. Giles tower, the Tron, Nelson Monument, and Holyrood. The Forth with Inchkeith and Largo Law are in the distance.
3. Salisbury Crags and Arthur's Seat to Carberry Hill, Portobello, Duddingston, the Bass, North Berwick Law, Prestonpans, Musselburgh, Traprain Law, and Craigmillar.
4. Liberton to the Braids and the Pentlands. Almost wholly pastoral, with shepherds and their flocks.

It is possible that this first effort did not entirely satisfy Lady Elton for three years later she sketched four more views, this time from the Calton Hill. They were engraved by J. Westall and are extremely useful from the topographic standpoint since they show the very considerable changes in the lay-out of the City during the thirty years which had elapsed since the Barker series of views. The sequence of the four views is outlined below :—

1. Prestonpans, Porto Bello, and Musselburgh Bay to Canongate Kirk. The background of Salisbury Crags and Arthur's Seat again proves most attractive. Flags, bunting and tents are prominent on the hillside where the Royal Artillery were

encamped in readiness to take part in the celebrations arranged for the Royal Visit of George IV in August, 1822. There are excellent views of Holyrood (with the Commendator's House) and the traffic in Regent's Road.

2. The town from the Canongate Kirk to Corstorphine Hill. This is a great sweeping view of the City set against the background of the Pentland Hills.

3. St. George's Church to Leith. The Leith section here is very similar to Barker's work. The Royal Squadron is at anchor in Leith Roads. Places of interest named include the Melville Monument, the Roman Catholic Chapel, St. Paul's Chapel in York Place, Ben Ledi, and the Ochil Hills.

4. View from the door of Nelson's Monument looking to the east. There is a military camp on the Hill and the officers and their young ladies are seen strolling about. Leith and its Glass Works, Lochend, Inchkeith, Portobello, and Musselburgh are all in the picture.

From the fact that three of the sections of this panorama depict the presence of the military in the City there can be little doubt that the drawings were largely inspired by the enthusiasm engendered by the prospect of the Royal Visit.

Between these two examples of the artistic ability of Lady Elton, Tytler George Tytler in 1822 drew on the spot his *Panoramic View of Edinburgh from the Calton Hill*. These three coloured lithographs, like those already mentioned, have distinct points of interest. The scene is set against Holyrood and Arthur's Seat. On the Calton Hill the ladies of the neighbourhood are examining their precious linen which has been set out to bleach on the grass. The road to Leith and the Glass Works of the Port are again a feature. Leith Roads is crowded with sailing ships, fishing smacks, and many types of small craft.

In 1841 J. W. Townsend produced his *Panorama from the Calton* Townsend *Hill*. It is one of the most interesting of all these panoramas by reason of the extraordinary scope of the print, with its wonderful variety of figures worked into the foreground, and the great detail in which the outstanding buildings and features of the landscape are given. The view is presented in a long narrow strip stretching from Hawkhill and Lochend to Leith Glass Works with the Pentland and Corstorphine

Hills as a background. All important points of interest are noted, many with unusual names and spellings—Kirkgotten Craigs [Caerketton] ; Edinr. Coal Gass Works ; Debtor's Jail [Calton Prison] ; and so on. On the hillside above the new High School is an animated scene showing boys playing football and a varied gallery of figures including kilted Highlanders, soldiers, fashionably dressed beaux and belles (the latter with their gaily coloured parasols), housewives busying themselves with their washing, and children of all ages playing about or seated with their parents. The general effect is one of animation contrasting sharply with the more formal landscapes of some of the other panoramic views.

Ebsworth   Though hardly panoramas in the sense that those already described may be so designated, a series of four water colours hung in Huntly House may well be considered here. These were done by Joseph W. Ebsworth in 1847 and depict the City as seen from the top of the Scott Monument. Only one of these drawings has been engraved in full size —the view from the upper gallery looking north over the New Town towards the Forth and the coast of Fife. It reproduces skilfully the atmosphere of Ebsworth's original sketch, with its lively picture of the street scenes and the open country beyond. North St. David's Street is crowded with all types of people—well-to-do citizens, working men and women, water caddies and the like, while further down the street the artist has cleverly sketched in a group of acrobats with an admiring audience enthralled by their gymnastic performances.

Of the three other sketches, that looking west shows the Mound with a regiment of soldiers marching down by the side of the Royal Institution and deploying into Princes Street. To the east the Calton Hill forms the background with the railway, Waverley Bridge, and Canal Street as notable features. The view to the south depicts the bold skyline of the Old Town, with the spires of the Tron, St. Giles, and the Tolbooth Churches silhouetted against the distant hills. These last three sketches were used as illustrations for J. H. A. Macdonald's *Life Jottings of an old Edinburgh Citizen*, where they are finely reproduced.

Greenwood   A similar series to that of Ebsworth was issued between 1841 and 1851 by C. J. Greenwood and engraved by R. S. Groom. They are as follows :—

1. From the Calton Hill. This is the usual view along Princes Street to the Castle.

2. Holyrood Palace and Arthur's Seat, from the Calton Hill. Regent Road looking towards the Palace and Chapel.
3. Old Town, Edinburgh, from Princes Street; The Bank of Scotland and the great sweep of the Mound; Horsemen and coaches add interest to the scene.
4. Portobello from the south east. Apparently the earliest of the four engravings, probably done about 1840. The seaside resort is seen from the south with cornfields in the foreground. Sailing ships and steamers are seen in the Firth.

About 1850 James Gordon, Jr. engraved his father's *Panoramic* Gordon *View from Nelson's Monument.* This was on the Barker scale as each lithographic section measured 22.3 inches by 14.2. Once again it is possible by comparison to note the changes wrought by time and the improver. The six sheets are

1. Looking west to the Melville Monument.
2. Looking south west. The Old and New Observatories on the Calton Hill itself are the most prominent features.
3. Looking north. Groups of figures and a carriage on the top of the Hill. The towns of Fife are all sketched in and are titled at the bottom of the print—Aberdour, Burntisland, Pettycur, Kinghorn, Kirkcaldy, and Dysart.
4. North east. Almost wholly given over to the National Monument and Short's Observatory. In the distance are faintly outlined the Bass Rock, Gulland Point, and Berwick Law.
5. South east. Towards Aberlady Bay.
6. Looking south. From the Crags to the College, with views of the Queen's Drive, Liberton, the New Prison, etc.

In 1851 H. G. Duguid did two aquatints in sepia from the Calton Duguid Hill—one looking towards Salisbury Crags from the south over St. Leonard's and the Braids, and the other westward along Princes Street. Taken together the two prints give a panoramic view of these parts of the City. No engraver's name is given.

Duguid did another sketch in 1851 entitled *Edinburgh from Braid Hills.* It was finely engraved by Christian Rosenbergh who is said to have employed artists in preparing the sketches which he afterwards aquatinted. Rosenbergh certainly worked in co-operation with

R. G. Reeve already mentioned. This scarce print shows Donaldson's Hospital to the extreme left; the three noted churches of St. John's, St. Cuthbert's, and St. George's; and the Castle. In the distance the coast of Fife is seen.

Sulman Coming down the years we have a very elaborate panoramic view of the City, which was issued by the *Illustrated London News* on July 18, 1868. It was done by John Sulman who depicts the burgh in a great sweep from Arthur's Seat to the West End with its fine Georgian terraces. The view is backed by the Grange and the Braids and the New Town streets take up the foreground. It is interesting to see what Lothian Road looked like before the building of the Usher Hall, and also to note the unusual lay-out of the gardens at Charlotte and St. Andrew's Squares. This is a most important illustration for reference purposes.

Dolby Another view of this type was drawn and engraved by E. T. Dolby and issued by M. & N. Hanhart, lithographic printers. It shows Edinburgh from the east side of the Calton Hill behind the terraced houses of Royal Terrace and Regent Road. It is undated but from the fact that only the central block of the Royal Infirmary is shown it must have been done about 1875. All the buildings on the top of the Calton Hill—Nelson's Monument, the National Monument, the Observatories—are featured. The fine terraces of London Road and those westward to the New Town give an impression of dignified planning.

Finally a *Panoramic View of Edinburgh from the North West* by Brewer H. W. Brewer and T. Griffiths was issued by *The Graphic* in 1886, the year of the great Exhibition in the Meadows. The viewpoint is the Caledonian Station Hotel with the Castle on the right and the Exhibition Hall clearly shown. At the foot of the illustration Burns' *Address to Edinburgh* and a numbered key block are given.

These panoramic views are most valuable for purposes of research as they show clearly the changing face of the City.

8

ROYAL VISITS

THE visit of George IV to the City in 1822 was the greatest social event during the first quarter of the century. The citizens expressed their loyalty to the throne and the King himself with the utmost enthusiasm. The decorations of the streets and buildings were on a scale that well-nigh baffled description. The Lord Provost, Magistrates and Council arranged functions and entertainments of all kinds to show their appreciation of the first Royal Visit to the City since the time of Charles I who was more concerned with religious and political dissensions in Scotland than in any friendly tour of the country.

The fullest record of the great occasion appears in an anonymous volume published in 1822 by Oliver and Boyd entitled *A Historical Account of His Majesty's Visit to Scotland*. The anonymous author of this work was Robert Mudie who spared no pains to set down a full and detailed description of the proceedings. His elaborate compilation is illustrated by four views depicting the outstanding incidents of the visit. The drawings engraved by W. H. Lizars, are listed below :—

(a) *The Landing of King George the IV, at Leith, 15 August, 1822.*
A tremendous crowd has gathered to give the initial welcome to His Majesty. As the King walks up the landing ramp, the escorting pinnaces with the oars of the crews raised in salute, the great crowds on the quayside and on the rigging of the ships in the harbour, and even on the roofs of the houses, give a striking impression of a great day in the history of the Port.

(b) *View of the Royal Procession advancing from Picardy Place from the barrier where the Keys of the City were delivered by the Lord Provost to His Majesty.*
Again a crowded scene with military escorts, flags flying, bands playing, windows and roof tops everywhere crowded with spectators, and all the pomp and ceremony of a Royal occasion.

(c) *View of the Grand Procession to the Castle where His Majesty has ascended to the Half Moon Battery.*

Rows of scaffolding, guards of honour both mounted and on foot, the State carriage, and the figure of the King on the Battery platform waving his hat to his subjects assembled in crowded masses below, combine to make a wonderful spectacle.

(d) *View of the Great Hall of the Parliament House, during the Banquet given by the City of Edinburgh to His Majesty King George IV, 24 August, 1822.*

The great banquet was served on a scale never before seen, within a room decorated with rich hangings everywhere, great illuminated chandeliers, beautifully chased candlesticks, and valuable gold plate. Nearly 300 guests were assembled on this great occasion to do honour to His Majesty.

In addition to these engravings of Lizars for Mudie's work there were other prints of the Royal Visit, among them a coloured aquatint by W. Turner de Lond—*Arrival of George IV at Palace of Holyrood, 1822*—a striking print measuring 22.5 inches by 14.8. It was dedicated to Lord Provost Sir William Arbuthnot, Bart. The State coach is drawn up at the entrance to the Palace and the whole courtyard is a seething mass of spectators behind whom the military uniforms of the escort can barely be seen. On the balconies and at every window the eager onlookers seek anxiously for a glimpse of His Majesty. The ladies seen in the foreground are most stylishly dressed and their colourful gowns add brightness to the darker tones of this fine print.

James Skene of Rubislaw expressed his interest in the visit by three sketches in water colour as noted below :—

(a) *The Landing of King George IV at Leith, Aug. 15th, 1822.*

A great number of craft fills the harbour and in the midst of them the King's barge, with the Royal Standard flying at the stern, can readily be identified. The Signal Tower and Custom House are prominent, while at the entrance to the dock the drawbridge is raised. Again spectators are everywhere to give His Majesty an overwhelming welcome. In the distance a great bonfire blazes on the summit of Arthur's Seat. The smoking kilns of the glass works are seen on the left.

PLATE 54

MINT CLOSE

After drawing by J. Skene. 1824

1**

PLATE 55

THE MEALMARKET, COWGATE

After drawing by I. Skene 1824

PLATE 56

Tolbooth of Leith

Water colour by J. Skene. 1818

House of Dean near
Edinr 9th 1826
19

PLATE 57

HOUSE OF DEAN

Water colour by J. Skene. 1826

PLATE 58

TRON CHURCH
Water colour by J. Skene. 1818

PLATE 59

LEITH WYND FROM THE NORTH
Water colour by J. Skene. 1817

PLATE 60

JOHNSTON TERRACE UNDER CONSTRUCTION

Water colour by J. Skene. 1829

Grass market

Heriots Bridge

PLATE 61

GRASSMARKET, SHOWING APPROACH TO HERIOT'S HOSPITAL BY
HERIOT BRIDGE

Water colour by J. Skene. N.d.

(b) *Removal of the Regalia of Scotland from the Castle preparatory to King George IV's arrival, August, 1822.*
The guard of Highlanders and other escort troops are seen passing through the inner gateway of the Castle.

(c) *George IV in the Castle*
The deep ditch, drawbridge, and ancient gateway are seen, while above on the platform prepared on the Half Moon Battery the King waves to the crowds below.

Skene did another water colour connected with George IV—*Proclaiming King George IV, Feb. 3rd, 1820, at the City Chambers.* In this drawing the building is seen in thick fog through which the arches of the Old Exchange appear crowded with interested citizens all come to pay their loyal tribute to the throne.

A pen and wash drawing by G. P. Reinagle entitled the *Landing of George IV at Leith* is a very pleasing item illustrating the great occasion. The artist has seized the moment when the King has just left the Royal barge and is being received by the Port dignatories. The yards and rigging of the ships in the harbour are lined with sailors anxious to get a glimpse of the King.

An engraving done much later than any of the above was after a drawing by T. Allom. The date was 1837 and the engraver J. Cousen. *The Canongate during the Procession of George IV (Edinburgh, Aug. 22, 1822,* is quite a neat and attractive print. Horsemen and soldiers precede the State coach as it passes the Tolbooth with its quaint Tower. In the distance the Tolbooth Church at the Castlehill is seen.

From this list we cannot omit the reproduction of Sir David Wilkie's picture of George IV being received by the Duke of Hamilton at Holyrood. As usual there are many spectators. Gaily uniformed trumpeters are sounding a spirited fanfare as the Duke bows low before the King and makes the presentation in the forecourt of the Royal Palace. On the left are Highlanders in their national dress with drawn swords and targes. Boys are seen clambering about on the projecting ledges of the pillars and waving flags. Altogether the scene is a picturesque and animated one.

Twenty years after the visit of George IV to the City, Queen Victoria and the Prince Consort travelled northwards to see their Scottish Capital. The tour began on an unfortunate note for Sir Robert Peel, who had charge of the arrangements, forgot to notify the municipal authorities of the time when the Queen was due to arrive at Granton and consequently there was no official reception party to receive the Royal pair. The Queen was very indignant at the slight and immediately drove on to Dalkeith Palace where she was to stay. Meantime Lord Provost Sir James Forrest had learned of the early arrival of Her Majesty and with the members of the Corporation he set off at high speed in the hope of intercepting the Royal carriage, but he had to return without having achieved his purpose. The Queen, on learning all the circumstances, agreed to another date for an official entry to the City and the usual ceremony of the presentation of the keys. The programme was duly carried out and the incident closed in a dignified manner. But later there appeared the ' Hey, Johnny Cope ' parodies and the biting cartoons. Two of these were issued in lithographic form and depict two stages of the Civic chase. One represents the Lord Provost and Magistrates humbly apologising to the Queen for not being in attendance at Granton; the other illustrates the hurried chase towards Dalkeith Palace.

The end of the visit saw the *Embarkation at Granton* which passed without mishap or special incident. This print shows H.M.S. Trident with yards manned and tremendous crowds gathered to give the Queen a Royal send-off. The Guard of Honour is there for inspection, boats are everywhere in the harbour to secure the best viewpoints, and the Royal visit comes to an end in true ceremonial fashion.

Other illustrations of this great event in the civic history are to be found in *Queen Victoria in Scotland, 1842*.

9

CITY CHARACTERS

A NUMBER of Edinburgh artists were greatly attracted by the characters who were to be seen in the streets of the Capital and devoted much of their time to depicting the eccentricities of these City 'oddities.' John Kay, Benjamin W. Crombie, and Ned Holt were the chief exponents of this type of work. Many of their sketches took the form of caricatures and cartoons, but others were straight studies of personalities who had played a prominent part in the history of the City.

A small volume entitled *Cries of Edinburgh characteristically represented accompanied with views of several principal buildings of the City* was published in 1803. There are twenty quaint woodcuts in the little brochure, each with a caption and a two line rhyme at the foot of the cut. The reproductions shown on the adjacent pages are re-drawings of some of the woodcuts in the volume.

The greatest creator of identifiable characters during the Golden Age was John Kay. Though born in Dalkeith in 1742 he spent most of his life in Edinburgh as a barber. No doubt he learned much from the social gossip associated with his occupation. While engaged in wig making he found time to draw in any medium available, and when the opportunity arose for him to start in business for himself in 1785 he still continued his favourite hobby of sketching. In his shop window wigs were replaced by drawings. The entertainment value of the latter must have been high for they attracted so much attention and favourable comment that he decided to confine himself to drawing and etching. Unfortunately his shop in Parliament Square was burnt down in the Great Fire of 1824 and he did not long survive the catastrophe.

Kay's widow lived until 1835 and shortly thereafter Hugh Paton, Carver and Gilder, issued a prospectus in the form of *A Descriptive Catalogue of Original Portraits, etc. drawn and etched by the late John Kay, caricaturist, Edinburgh.* It was an advance advertisement for a

Kay

series of parts, quarto in size, each containing approximately ten etchings, with letterpress and anecdotes relating to the subjects illustrated in the parts. The *Catalogue* is dated 1836. It is a substantial list of 25 pages with details of 356 etchings.

Paton had the good fortune to secure the services at a very low salary of James Paterson, a competent journalist, who had a real flair for tracking down local gossip and working up the details, if not in scholarly fashion, most certainly in a style which lent itself to those ' anecdotal biographies ' which have proved invaluable to all recorders of local history since they were written to accompany Kay's inimitable drawings. James Maidment, the eminent antiquary, also shared in the work.

The parts were issued as advertised, and the completed work in two great volumes in 1837-8. Further editions were published from time to time, but most of these later issues were done in poorer style and in some cases were greatly abridged.

Kay is said to have etched nearly 900 plates, and probably no set of character sketches of similar magnitude has been produced elsewhere in the country. The plates and accompanying letterpress have a double interest—biographical and artistic—and it is no easy matter to decide which of these aspects is the more valuable. Certainly both illustrations and text provide highly entertaining material for the student of local history.

The collection of etched portraits form a wonderful gallery of Edinburgh notabilities of the late 18th century. It would be useless to name here all those who appeared in the work—let it suffice to say that the pages include law lords, antiquaries, authors, philosophers, scientists, clergymen, travellers, booksellers, criminals, and even idiots. Yet, oddly enough, important people are omitted. Miss Louise Ross in an article in *Chambers's Journal, April, 1934,* points out that there is no portrait of Burns in the gallery. She also draws attention to the fact that " his sketch of Adam Smith is the only authentic likeness of the author of *The Wealth of Nations.*" Kay did not restrict himself to Edinburgh for he has a fine etching of *The Sapient Septemviri,* a portrait group of seven learned professors of King's College, Aberdeen; another of James Bruce, the Abyssinian traveller; and *The Daft Highland Laird,* James Robertson of Kincraigie in Perthshire. Nor did he confine himself to portraits of individuals for we find in the pages examples of his sly humour in the sketches entitled *Before Marriage* and *Lawyer and Client.* In the first case we have the smiling faces of the happy couple, but by reversing the print two dismal countenances indicate the sad results of matrimony. The other etching illustrates the cheerful and smiling lawyer, while the reversal presents the gloomy looks of the client whose " guid gangin' plea " is proving a financial disaster. In another sketch entitled *The Five Alls* the artist sets out five figures in five separate strips each with a special heading as follows :—

I pray for all
I plead for all
I maintain all
I fight for all
I take all.

The last strip is a picture of the Devil seeking his prey.

Another drawing entitled *The Diamond Beetle Case* is a delightful caricature and legal skit in the form of a group of fifteen legal luminaries at the last sitting of the Old Court of Session, 11th of July, 1808 gravely discussing an action of " defamation and damages, Alexander Cunningham, Jeweller in Edinburgh, against James Russell, Surgeon there." A numbered key gives the clue to the names of the famous judges in this interesting contribution to the gallery.

Of quite different type is *The Evening Walk,* a sketch of the local dandies with their ladies strolling past Princes Street Coffee House. The recumbent figure draping himself against the railings is worth noting. No. 1 Princes Street was the Coffee House and No. 2 the Crown Hotel. No. 36 Princes Street was the Star Hotel. Within comparatively recent times it was occupied by the business of Messrs. Renton's, Ltd. and now by C. & A. Modes.

An interesting assessment of Kay's work is given by Mr. John C. Guy in his article on *Edinburgh's Engravers* in the *Book of the Old Edinburgh Club,* volume 9, 1916. He asserts that " as prints probably the best are those of Mary Queen of Scots; the King, Queen and Dauphin of France; and the Dog and Cat Fight, all of which appear in the appendix to the second volume, because they ' could not with propriety be introduced into a work of Original Portraits.' " One hesitates to accept that statement without qualification as the general standard of many of the portraits is so high. At the same time most critics would readily agree that the print *Maria Scotorum Regina et Franciae Dotaria* is a fine etching, and that of the *King, Queen & Dauphin of France* a perfect cameo. The *Dog and Cat Fight* to which Guy refers is apparently *Dead Game* which represents a keen struggle between the two contestants for possession of a tasty meal. In this print the author's favourite cat is introduced.

Three excellent examples of Kay's work are hung in Huntly House —hand-coloured etchings of City Magistrates wearing their robes of office. They are Sir John Marjoribanks, holding in his hand a plan of Regent Bridge and the New Jail; Sir James Stirling, Bart. looking out through a window at the Old Town; and Sir Thomas Elder of Forneth.

In addition to the items already described mention must be made of an important volume in the Edinburgh Room containing 80 of John Kay's etchings and 16 original drawings in colour and 4 prints by William Kay—all first rate examples of the work of the two brothers. William concentrated on studies of the town crier, water caddie, coal man, street porter, a member of the City Guard, and similar street characters.

Crombie   Somewhat later than Kay Benjamin W. Crombie was responsible for a remarkable series of etched caricatures, executed between 1837 and 1847. The sketches were first issued in parts until 1839, and the first edition appeared in book form in 1844. It consisted of 21 plates with two portraits on each page, 42 in all. They made a most attractive volume with the title *Modern Athenians*. After Crombie's death in 1847 H. Paton purchased the etched copper-plates from his widow and issued further editions, the last of which was that of 1882 edited by William Scott Douglas. In his biographical preface Douglas says that the etchings were superior in treatment to the work of Kay and less given to caricature. The first part of the statement one can readily accept but as one looks through the volume there is plenty of evidence that Crombie was keenly observant in seizing upon the peculiarities of his 'sitters.' Paton must have been pleased with the success of Paterson's notes to the plates of Kay for in this 1882 edition of Crombie he adopted the same plan and thus added greatly to the reference value of the work. The double portraits on each plate illustrate the Pickwickian figure of Dr. David Dickson *vis-à-vis* Dr. Candlish; genial countenanced Lt.-General Ainslie facing the dour Bindon Blood ; the self-important Robert Thomson, Sheriff of Caithness followed by the prim and proper monocled Sheriff of Bute; Hugo Arnot in his tartan trews and muffled stock—as thin as a rake—and the corpulent John Irvine of Bonshaw; and by no means least John Sheriff, otherwise known as Dr. Syntax because of his likeness to Rowlandson's famous figure of fun. The character and idiosyncracies of this extraordinary man are admirably described by the editor, and in similar style we have a vivid picture of that strange personality Bindon Blood who was a real bibliomaniac and a sad problem for the auctioneers and booksellers of the City. He was variously known as 'the Vampire' and 'the Dragon' and though a great book collector he was most grudging in lending any of his treasures. On being approached by a scholar for the loan of a work of which he possessed the only two copies known the scholar received such a surly reception that he is reported to have said " I might as well ask him to make me a present of his brains and reputation."

The frontispiece of the 1882 edition is a full length study of Sir Walter Scott in characteristic pose—an exceedingly pleasing example of portraiture.

The sketches form another colourful gallery of Edinburgh characters and the trained eye of the artist has carefully emphasised those features of his selected victims in a way that delights the less observant but interested reader. In many ways we could well claim that these drawings are precursors of that famous caricaturist of Victorian times— Spy of *Vanity Fair*.

In addition to the set described above the Library also possesses 28 small original pencil sketches by Crombie many of which do not appear in *Modern Athenians* but may well have been the preliminary drawings for other plates for a new edition.

The work of Ned Holt is not of the same high standard as that of Kay and Crombie but he did many water colour sketches of well-known City characters and a volume of 49 of these items, illustrating such street figures as Coco Nut Tam, Daddy Flockhart, Sarah Sibbald, Old Malabar, Tory Gunn, Kirsty Veitch (Burn the Bible), Register Rachel, Daft Jamie, Heather Jock, Blind Hughie serves as a record of those quaint individuals who were familiar to the Edinburgh citizens.

Holt

10

SKENE DRAWINGS OF OLD EDINBURGH

On 24th February 1943 the Public Libraries Committee purchased at Dowell's sale three volumes of water-colour drawings by James Skene of Rubislaw. The drawings number 222 in all. Most of them illustrate buildings and views of Edinburgh between the years 1817-19, though there is one as early as 1804 and some of date as late as 1837.

As far as can be ascertained, the drawings remained in Skene's possession until his death in 1864 when they were acquired by Bailie Dunlop, a property valuator in the City, a keen collector, and an antiquary of considerable repute. This statement is vouched for by the entry in the preface to George Lorimer's *Early Days of St. Cuthbert's Church, Edinburgh* (1915), in which the author acknowledges the kindness of Mr. Mercer Dunlop " in allowing me to make use of the views of Old St. Cuthbert's, originally forming part of the collection of James Skene of Rubislaw, which was acquired by the late Bailie Dunlop."

The drawings remained in the possession of the Dunlop family until the sale in 1943. Bailie John Charles Dunlop was a brother of Alison Hay Dunlop who, with him, prepared *The Book of Old Edinburgh* for the International Exhibition of Industry held in the Meadows in 1886 and was also the author of another interesting work *Anent Old Edinburgh*.

James Skene of Rubislaw was born in 1775. His father died next year, and in 1783 the family removed from Aberdeen to Edinburgh, primarily for educational reasons, and took a lease of Shawfield's Lodging in Riddel's Court, near the ancient Weigh House. Even at that early age the artistic bent of the young lad showed itself, and he tells how he made his early drawings on a broad cellar door of the house with whiting as his medium. His first efforts included sketches of near-by houses in the West Bow and other picturesque buildings in the

PLATE 62

BRISTO PORT AND CHARITY WORKHOUSE

Water colour by J. Skene. N.d.

PLATE 63

KIRKGATE OF LEITH

Water colour by J. Skene. 1818

neighbourhood. About this time [1785] the project for the building of the South Bridge was set on foot. This ultimately led to the disappearance of many notable landmarks such as the Black Turnpike a matter of great regret to Skene who had actually lived for a short time in that famous old building.

As his talent developed Skene took every possible opportunity of setting down on paper his impressions of the outstanding features of the Old Town during the late 18th and early 19th centuries. Later on, with the rise of the New Town, the family moved to George Street, opposite the Assembly Rooms, and Skene was again right in the centre of those great new planning developments which were transforming the City. It was fortunate for us that he lived through this wonderful period in the history of the City, for his facile pen and brush have provided us with an enthralling series of views of the disappearing and changing face of Scotland's capital. His interest in the architectural antiquities of 'Auld Reekie' never waned, and a year after his death his great friend Sir David Brewster, in an address to the Royal Society of Edinburgh, placed on record that

"During his residence in Edinburgh, Mr. Skene explored and sketched the various buildings in the Old Town that were remarkable for their antiquity or historical interest, and he has left a valuable collection of these sketches, which we trust may be given to the public."

Seventy-eight years were to elapse before Sir David's remarks bore fruit, but the collection is now safely housed where it can be freely consulted by all.

At the age of 21 Skene went to Germany to further his studies and on his return he was admitted to the Scottish Bar in 1797. Thus began his acquaintance with Sir Walter Scott; the friendship ripened with the passing years and was to continue throughout the remainder of Scott's life. They had a common bond in their love of German literature; indeed Scott had begun his literary career with translations from Bürger in 1796 and his better known rendering of Goethe's *Goetz von Berlichingen* in 1799. From time to time Scott saw and greatly admired Skene's drawings, and in 1806, writing to Lady Dalkeith, he describes Skene as " an amiable and accomplished young man, and for a gentleman the best draughtsman I ever saw." Between this date and 1820 Skene completed at least 120 drawings of the City, the bulk of them in the years 1817-19, and it would appear to have been about this time that Scott's interest in them was so greatly aroused that he repeatedly discussed with Skene the historical incidents and anecdotes connected with the scenes represented, and indeed suggested that together they might produce a monthly publication entitled *Reekieana* for which Skene would do the drawings and Scott the text. During this time Skene had been experimenting with the comparatively new medium of lithography [invented in 1796], no doubt with a view to making use of it for the proposed publication, and on 22nd August 1820 we find him writing to Scott with the news that he is taking Mrs. Skene abroad for the sake of her health, and adds :

"I have been doing some little things in Lithography of which I send you a specimen of my first attempt.... There are errors in the Etching I send, but I was working in the dark as it is my first Lithographical attempt and I see that they can be easily avoided."—*Walpole Collection.*

Scott's reply to this letter was characteristic of him. It is from Abbotsford and is dated 29th August 1820, and is in these terms :

"MY DEAR SKENE.—It is a sad thing that you are obliged to begin your rambles again, but prevention is better than cure, and much as I shall feel your absence, and that of my much-esteemed friend Mrs. Skene, I must comfort myself by thinking that you are amused both of you, and her health strengthened and confirmed. If I take the Continent, which I should wish greatly, I will not fail to direct my course so as to insure our meeting, for you will scarce choose a nook in the Continent where I will not poke you out.... The specimen of lithography is capital, but when shall we set about our ' Antiquitates Reekianae ? ' When indeed ? Meanwhile I hope you will not fail to add to your stock of drawings whatever memorables may occur in your travels. The etching was very clever indeed. God bless you, my dear Skene, your excellent partner and your family, and send us a speedy and a happy meeting. All here, Lockharts included, send kindest regards.—I am, very truly and affectionately yours,

WALTER SCOTT."

The Continental journey with Skene was never to be made, much to Skene's disappointment, but in speaking of this letter in his *Papers* Skene says :

" The ' Antiquitates Reekianae ' was a joint undertaking of Sir Walter's and mine, illustrative of the ancient history, manners and antiquities of Edinburgh, but the necessity of my going abroad at that time delayed its appearance, and before I returned at the lapse of a year and a half, circumstances had occurred altogether to prevent its publication. The drawings I had prepared for the purpose had been seen, and the delay gave time for the idea to be taken up and turned to use by others, without, however, the only part of the scheme which would probably have given it interest in the public eye, the narrative part from Sir Walter's pen."

The others referred to were probably Storer whose *Views in Edinburgh* was published in 1820; and W. H. Lizars, who issued two publications in 1825—*Edinburgh Delineated,* and *Picturesque Views of Edinburgh.* Though the last two items are dated 1825 it should be noted that the *Picturesque Views* was issued in monthly parts from July 1823 onwards, and it was produced exactly in the style which had been laid down for the Skene-Scott project. Lizars must therefore have been working on the plates some considerable time before the issues of the parts, and Skene not only knew of this but bitterly resented the fact that his cherished plans were thus being frustrated. He made a last effort, however, to proceed with his idea, and on 28th March 1823 we find him sending to Scott a lengthy and detailed letter with proposals for the publication, estimates of costs, and three specimen lithographic illustrations for the work. This letter and the accompanying lithographic impressions are in the Edinburgh Room at the Central Library. As far as I know the letter has never been published, but it is of such importance that it warrants quotation in full. It is as follows :

Edinr. 28 March, 1823.

" My dear Scott,
    I send a specimen of Reekieana for your inspection, likewise a list of the materials already in my collection with an indication of a few of the subjects of historical anecdote to which they may bear reference.

that you may guess at their sufficiency or not, to the sort of structure you contemplated.

The plates are my first experiment in an art new to me, therefore some improvement may be looked for as the difficulties are progressively overcome, and the ease of a sure and bold touch worked out, for there is no one here capable of giving any insight into the little, yet very essential arcana that attend the practice of every art. There is an other thing to be attended to unfavourable to first impressions, which these I send you are, that it is different from Copper plate engraving where the proofs on first impression are the finest, in Lithography on the contrary, they are the worst, the first twenty or thirty impressions are either faint or harsh and unequal, until the stone becomes firmly and uniformly charged with ink, so as to bring all the parts into harmony, so that future impressions would be preferable to those I send you. Another circumstance and a more important one is the uncertainty attending the printer's success, as those we have here are far from expert, accordingly you will observe that Regent Murray's house is much injured in the throwing off. It was the last I did, and by far the best, so far as my part of the work was concerned so that I was much disappointed at the result, and the printer honestly confessed to me that he had botched it. I hope however to improve it by retouching. The other two [Cardinal Beaton's Palace and Haddo's Hole] are very well for first attempts. I showed them to Lockhart who was much pleased with them, and said that if you brought Reekieana into action he would help to change the piece. Now from your Potosi of historical anecdote I have no doubt you could send forth a most entertaining little budget, and my Lithographs would be a sort of toast to introduce the good liquor like the quotations from old plays that are often so obliging as to prepare us for the treat to follow.

It appears to me that a set of periodical *livraisons* consisting of 6 engravings in octavo, perhaps two of them smaller than the others as vignettes with as much letterpress as you please ; and perhaps a couple of characteristic groups or heads of remarkable by-gone characters from Lockhart, or anything else amusing would be easily accomplished. For such I could furnish regularly Lithographs for at least twenty Nos. I purchased a stock of stone and materials at Munich the expense of printing and paper would be very trifling :

The price of each stone comes to about	£— : 10 : —
Printing 300 impressions	— : 12 : —
Plained paper for 300	— : 15 : —
	£1 : 17 : —
Six plates in each No.	6
	£11 : 2 : —

There is no other expense but that of my labour and skill which of course is invaluable, but to tell the truth there is a good deal of labour and time required in these engravings. I find that I require four forenoons for each, but in these times when tenants have got out of the way of paying rents, it would be far from inconvenient if the occupation of my forenoons were anyhow to turn to profitable account, which none of my occupations as yet have ever had the sense to accomplish. So that if Reekieana still finds favour in your sight, and is likely to be worth your while, and my humbler efforts, I shall be ready to work away upon any of the subjects you like, as I think I have now ascertained that I shall be able to make Lithography suit the purpose of these minute town views, of which I had some doubts. The selection for each No. depending more upon the subject for the pen than the pencil, could easily be arranged, suppose the first to be the Frontispiece of Holyrood Gate— Old Cross vignette—Beaton's Palace—Haddo's hole—Regent Murray —and the Maiden.

I think you suggested that it might issue from under the wing of the Bannatyne according to regulations 11th and 12 having a few extra copies on large paper for the club, and a larger impression on common paper to defray the expense and profit.

I intended to have sent you a few ideas as to the emblem for the Club title-page and a Colophon, pencil ideas I mean, but I have not yet got anything to please me. I think some use could be made of the Phenix surviving from its ashes, however I shall try two or three concerts.

I was very sorry to learn the loss of my old friend your Brother. I had never seen him since he first left Edinr. full of health and hilarity —poor little Walter will now if possible cling the closer to his second father and I shall be much mistaken in my augury if he does not turn out remarkably well.

With best compliments to the Ladies.

I remain,

Yours very sincerely,

(Sgd.) JAMES SKENE.

I sent a few ideas about the Garden last week, which I suppose you got."

This self-revealing document shows that Skene placed no mean valuation on his artistic ability and that he was not averse to putting it to good account. Nor was he satisfied to leave any stone unturned if he could further the project which lay so near to his heart. The list of which he speaks in the first paragraph was a lengthy one of some 97 drawings which he had carefully selected from the sketches which he had already prepared. It was set out in double columns; the first giving the titles of the 97 drawings, and the second the notes of anecdotes and incidents connected with each, which Scott was to elaborate for the proposed work. The detailed list is as follows :

REEKIANA

DRAWINGS	CONNECTED WITH ANECDOTES OF
1 Archepiscopal Palace, Cowgate	Cardinal Beaton, Sharp, etc.
2 Haddo's Hole, St. Giles	Who ?—Contiguous to the Tolbooth—Viaticum of the condemned.
3 Regent Murray's House, Cannongate	Murray—Montrose—Argyle.
4 Earl Huntley's Do.	Do.
5 Hotel for foreign Ambassadors	Netherbow.
6 Generals Court, Potterrow	Monke—Jacob More.
7 Kirk of field	Darnley etc. Principal Robertson.
8 Hamilton House	Earl of Arran—College—Jas. 6 disputations.

DRAWINGS	CONNECTED WITH ANECDOTES OF
9 Knox's house—pulpit, etc.	Do. Reformation Covenant.
10 The Maiden. Juggs. Thumbscrews &c.	
11 Heart of Midlothian. two	
12 . . . . . . Cage	
13 Oratory of Mary of Guise	under protection of the castle. Jealousies of the French troops etc.
14 Court house of Leith	built by her.
15 Holyrood House & chapel	various drawings connected with its various history from the legend of David 2nd to the court of Geo. 4th.
16 Outer Gate of the Palace	
17 Girth Cross	Sanctuary. Debtor chase. etc.
18 Water Gate	Hospital of St. Thomas—pond.
19 Remains of the Catchpel or	Tennis court of the Palace.—a grotesque old turret. Comely Garden.
20 Castle. various drawings	
Morton's prison	attack of the castle. Kirkaldie etc.
Regalia discovered	Drochil Castle.
Removal to Holyrood	
From the west port	Battle of Boroughmoor; retreat of French to the rock. Etc.
Spur	Sheepskirmish. etc.
Halfmoon battery	Kings reception—Mounts Meg.
several others—	illuminated etc.
21 Well house tower	North Loch, its history.
22 Grass Market	West port 1745—Kings stables. —Tilting field now a square of slaughterhouses. — Kings Grange. Old gallows and its annals.—Porteous, etc.
23 Monastery of Gray Friars. Dominicans	Their humility in refusing to reside in so splendid a mansion.

DRAWINGS	CONNECTED WITH ANECDOTES OF
24 Herriots work	Old Bridge—Templars & Knights of St. John.
25 West Bow, various drawings	Major Weir—remains of the antient gate—Assembly rooms,
26 Weigh House. two.	
27 Castle Hill. Old Castle Gate	remains of chapels & wall, etc.
28 Land Market	Its former gentility—scene of several affrays of old time.
29 Lukenbooths	
30 Libertons Wynde	
31 St. Giles. various drawings	Towns charter chamber. Oratory. Jenny Geddes—Fate of the saint and abbot of Nismes—The Virgins shrine—Goldsmiths hall—The Creems.—Parliament etc.
32 Parliament house. Old facade	sculpture and statue.
33 Parliament House during Musical festival	
34 Parliament house. Kings banquet. etc.	
35 Parliament house from the Cowgate	in its old form.
36 Back stairs	site of old Holyrood chapel—St. Giles church yard vaulted—The farm house of St. Giles grange was here.
37 Old Cross	The prophetic vision.
38 Exchange. proclamation of	Geo. 4th.
39 Old guard house. 1514.	piquet horse—clans shell turnpike. Maison Dieu.
40 Tron Kirk before the South Bridge	Christ Kirk—pillory.—old Dress & Equipages—booth of the old corporation of sweeps.
41 Netherbow port	Cannongate. Monks market.

DRAWINGS	CONNECTED WITH ANECDOTES OF
42 Cannongate Tolbooth & Cross	
43 White horse tavern	Dr. Johnson.
44 Cowgate port	Priory of St. Mary of Placentia.
45 Mint	
46 Black Friars monastry	Colege wynde — indulgencies advertised on the door.
47 House of the 12 Apostles. Cowgate.	probable a manor house before the street was built.
48 French Ambassadors Hotel	
49 Mary Magdalain	Maison Dieu.
50 Old Fish Market close	privileges of the hangman.
51 Various drawings of Cowgate	architecture.
52 Gray Friars church & yard	Covenanters monument.
53 Bloody Mackenzies grave	
54 Cordiners Hall	Duke of Douglas's house.
55 Potterrow	
56 Nunnery of the Sheens	
57 Chapel of St. Roque	plague—Blackford Hill. Grange. Borough moor—heere stane, etc.
58 St. Leonards	Templars of Mounthooly—Cemetery of Quakers. Suicedes & unbaptised children.
59 Craig Millar	Mary etc.
60 Arthur's Seat & Salisbury Crag	various
61 St. Anthony's chapel	
62 Gilmerton	
63 Restalrig	Logan.
64 St. Margarets Well	
65 Trinity Colege kirk	Mary of Guelders Queen of Jas 2d.

	DRAWINGS	CONNECTED WITH ANECDOTES OF
66	Do. Hospital	Library various—Refectory like the main deck of a man of war. little change of the monkish forms.
67	Paul's work. 12 Beads men	Bishop Spense.
68	Calton Prison	
69	Low Calton	
70	North Bridge	
71	Regents Bridge	Dingwal castle at the orphan Hospital.
72	Humes Monument	
73	Leith Wynde. old wall, &	Dung port & postern at Halkerstons wynde.
74	New town various.	Gabriels lane & Barefoot parks probably broad pond.
75	Dudingstone	
76	Cannon mills	
77	Craig Lockhart	
78	South Leith Kirk	
79	Jas. 6th Hospital	
80	Citadel of Leith	Old Noll.
81	North Leith various	
83	Royston where the troops	sent by Henry 8th landed. burnt Edinr.
84	Lauriston	Law of Do.
85	Cramond. Roman	
86	Loch End. Skating	
87	St. Bernards well	
88	Princes Street	
89	Wrytes houses. 1376	Robt. 3rd. Jas. 4 & 6.
90	Merchiston	Napier
91	Tolbooth Musselburg	Inveresk Roman
92	Inch Garvie	
93	Inch Colm	
94	Inch Keith	Besieged by Dessè. Guerres d'Ecosse.

Drawings	Connected with anecdotes of
95 Tolbooth Well. P.P.C.	
96 Corstorphin	Templars.
97 Old sculpture & Inscriptions. various.	

A week passed before Scott answered Skene's letter in these terms

" My dear Skene,—I received your parcel safe, and I have no doubt whatever that the ' Reekianae ' will answer, so very beautiful are the specimens you have supplied. Three hundred copies appears rather a large impression, but we will see what Constable says. The man of books is to be here on Wednesday or Thursday next, and I will take the opportunity to take his advice about it, for a man can no more be delivered of a book without a bookseller than a woman of a child without an accoucheur, and much trouble and risk is saved in both cases by having recourse to the first assistance. Constable and Dr. Hamilton are worth all the old women in the world.

Lockhart, I am sure, will not want good-will, but I doubt if his very excellent sketches are finished enough for publication. Charles Sharpe's assistance would be truly invaluable, both in explanation and delineation."

In a further letter to Skene he says :

" I have given Constable the plates, and he seems much pleased with the plan of the ' Reekianae.' All that I can do will be done, of course. He will hold communication with you on the subject himself. I conceive that it should be something that would pay your time and trouble."

In spite of Sir Walter's warm advocacy of the proposed book the whole project had to be abandoned because, as Skene tells us in his *Papers* :

" Mr. Constable's proposals which were something of the wolf's division usual to booksellers and often oppressive to the many authors who engage in such compacts, were not to be risked."

What this " Wolf's division to booksellers " consisted of I have been unable to discover, but it is scarcely surprising that Constable, who had so recently as 1820 published Storers *Views in Edinburgh* in two large quarto volumes with finely engraved plates and plans as well as extensive letterpress, should have been somewhat reluctant to embark upon another venture of a similar nature, more particularly as Skene, on his own admission, was not yet satisfied that he had attained sufficient skill in delineating landscapes in the new medium with which he was experimenting. Be that as it may, nothing more appears to have been done at that time and Scott's financial disaster in 1826 put an end to further progress. But Skene kept adding to his drawings from time to time, and since he could no longer count on the help of Sir Walter for the text he required he apparently undertook the task of compiling the material himself. But a further event was to cause him considerable pain, for in 1833 Robert Chambers issued his *Reekiana : Minor Antiquities of Edinburgh,* in the preface of which he speaks thus :

" Reekiana—a title once contemplated for a similar work by Sir Walter Scott, and which he good-humouredly surrendered to me some years ago—is probably the last contribution I shall make to the history of Edinburgh."

To Skene this was surely " the unkindest cut of all." The plan of his long cherished work had been adopted by Lizars; now the very title itself had been selected by Chambers for a similar publication. What more could he do ? Very little indeed; and, though he added one or two more drawings of the City to his collection, neither they nor the manuscript, carefully written in his own neat script and bound up in leather, were to be given to the people in his lifetime. From my own examination of the manuscript I must say it will be a pity if it does not appear in some permanent form, either as a separate publication or as one of the volumes issued under the auspices of the Old Edinburgh Club. In either form it would serve as a fitting memorial, if that were needed, of one who dearly loved this ancient City of Edinburgh and did everything in his power to place on record his own impressions of its glory.

When we come to look at the drawings two points at once stand out : first, that they give a wonderfully complete contemporary survey of Edinburgh in the early nineteenth century, and second, that they undoubtedly have a high artistic value. Scott was a man of sound judgment and his oft-expressed view that Skene was the best amateur draughtsman in the country is, I think, borne out by a close examination of this collection of his work. Skene had his limitations, but his sense of colour, his appreciation of the architectural refinement of the subjects he chose for his pen and brush, and above all his technique give him a high place among the artists who specialised in this kind of work. Unfortunately he was not equally skilled in the art of engraving and his attempts to master lithographic methods of reproduction did not lead him very far. As a consequence, I have no doubt the high costs involved in getting his work engraved was the real difficulty which he encountered when he sought to commercialise his art.

On examination of these 220 drawings the Edinburgh expert will notice that though a high proportion of them must have been done from the actual buildings and scenes as they existed in Skene's own day, others represent places which had been demolished before his time. These he must have prepared from drawings or similar material collected from various sources. One must remember that Skene was much nearer in time to the days of Edinburgh's greatness, and his personal contacts with eminent people and events gave him a quite exceptional opportunity of exercising his talents on this wonderful set of drawings.

Those who wish to examine the drawings which comprise the complete set, can inspect them in the Edinburgh Room, where they will have access to a very fully annotated list of the series. The notes to each drawing, mainly historical and topographical in nature, were compiled by Mr. Charles B. Boog Watson, an Honorary Vice-President of the Old Edinburgh Club, and a frequent contributor to its publications.

The manuscript of *Antiquitates Reekianae* is also now in the Edinburgh Room where it can be consulted at any time.

11

BIBLIOGRAPHY

THIS monograph could easily have been considerably extended but it is felt that enough has been said to indicate the scope of the print collection in the Edinburgh Room. For further study of the subject the following references may be found of use :—

Architectural Institute of Scotland, 1865. Edinburgh: its houses and its noted inhabitants, chiefly those of the 17th and 18th centuries. Catalogue of original drawings, engravings, etc. . . . selected from the private collection of W. F. Watson. Prepared by Mr. Watson. Privately printed.

Book of the Old Edinburgh Club.

Bushnell, George H. *comp.* Scottish engravers. 1949.

Cameron, James. A Bibliography of Slezer's *Theatrum Scotiae.*

Cowan, William. Early views and plans of Edinburgh. 1909.

Cowan, William and Inglis, H. R. The early views and maps of Edinburgh. Royal Scottish Geographical Society. 1919.

Edinburgh Public Libraries Committee. The Edinburgh scene : catalogue of prints and drawings in the Edinburgh Room, Central Public Library. 1951.

Gordon, T. Crouther. David Allan of Alloa, 1744-1796, the Scottish Hogarth. 1951.

Guy, John C. Edinburgh engravers. In *Book of the Old Edinburgh Club,* Vol. 9, 1916, pp. 79-113.

MacGeorge, A. William Leighton Leitch, landscape painter. 1884.

Morris, Roy. The etchings of Walter Geikie, R.A. In *Print Collector's Quarterly,* Vol. 22, 1935.

Oppé, A. P. The drawings of Paul and Thomas Sandby in the collection of His Majesty the King at Windsor Castle. 1947.

Print Collector's Quarterly.

Rawlinson, W. C. The engraved work of J. M. W. Turner, R.A. 1913. 2 vols.

Sanderson, Kenneth. Some topographical prints of Edinburgh. In *Print Collector's Quarterly,* Jan., 1935.

Wilson, Sir Daniel. Ancient maps and views of Edinburgh. In his Memorials of Edinburgh in the olden time, Vol. 2. pp. 279-84.

INDEX

INDEX

Rose, J. — 77
Rosenbergh, C. — 85-6
Ross, T. — 78
Runciman, A. — 17
Runciman, J. — 17-18, 54, 78

Sandby, P. — 19-22, 29, 32
Sargent, F. J. — 41
Sawers, L. — 77
Schenck and McFarlane — 32, 68
Scott, D. — 37
Scott, R. — 33, 35-6, 40, 43, 47
Scott, W. B. — 36-7
Shepherd, T. H. — 55-6
Skene, J. — 4, 5, 39, 63, 73, 88-89, 96-108
Slezer, J. — 11-13
Smeall, W. — 57
Smith, Mrs. J. S. — 78
Smith, W. R. — 56
Somerset, Duke of. *See* Hertford, Earl of
Somerville, D. — 47-8
Sparrow, — — 28
Stanfield, C. — 57, 63, 69-70
Steuart, J. — 79
Steuart, T. — 77
Stevenson, J. — 36
Stewart, M. *See* Elton, Lady
Storer, J. and H. S. — 48-9, 99, 106

Sulman, J. — 86
Summers, T. — 13
Sutherland, T. — 50
Swarbreck, S. D. — 64

Thomson, C. — 59
Thomson, Rev. J. — 46-7, 60
Townsend, J. W. — 83-4
Turner, J. M. W. — 59-60, 63, 75
Turner, W. — 60-62, 88
Tytler, G. — 83

Van Dalen, C. — 6
Van den Hoyen, R. — 9-10

Walker, J. — 26
Wallis, R. — 59, 60
Webster, M. — 62
West, J. — 65
Wilkie, Sir D. — 24, 31, 75, 89
Williams, H. W. — 39, 60, 63
Wilson, A. — 35, 36, 43
Wilson, Sir D. — 47, 68-9
Winkles, H. — 53
Wit, F. de. *See* De Wit, F.
Woollett, W. — 25
Woolnoth, W. — 46

Yeates, — — 10-11